THE COURT OF KING ARTHUR

THE SCRIBNER SERIES
FOR YOUNG PEOPLE
EACH WITH ILLUSTRATIONS IN COLOR

CHARLES SCRIBNER'S SONS

"Like the halo of a saint."

THE COURT
OF KING ARTHUR

STORIES FROM THE LAND OF
THE ROUND TABLE

BY

WILLIAM HENRY FROST

ILLUSTRATED BY SYDNEY RICHMOND BURLEIGH

NEW YORK
CHARLES SCRIBNER'S SONS
1916

to

My Aunt

Josephine Wakefield Collins

MY EARLIEST COMPANION AND

GUIDE IN LANDS OF

WONDERS

CONTENTS

ILLUSTRATIONS

BEFORE WE SET OUT

IF you are to follow our journey in the Land of the Round Table, you must know at the start that there are other guides there than I. You do know them, or some of them, already, I suppose—older, wiser, better guides than I. They have been my guides on many happy journeys in that land, and they will be yet, I hope, on many more. First of them always, in my thought, though not in time, is the gentle knight Sir Thomas Malory. No one else has ever told so much of King Arthur and told it so well as he. Older than he—oldest of them all—was Nennius, and then there was Geoffrey of Monmouth, who wrote a delightful book, with nothing else so delightful in it as the joke of calling it a history. After him came Wace and the good priest Layamon, to whom surely the Lord was merciful. There were many whose names we do not know, and some whose names we cannot even guess at.

There were the makers of those wonderful stories called the Mabinogion, which Lady Charlotte Guest has let us look over her boys' shoulders to read. If every mother could make such a gift to her children as this of Lady Charlotte Guest's, how rich the world would be! Sometimes as I rewrote the stories that she has rewritten, I could scarcely help using her very words, because it seemed that to use any other words than hers would hurt the story. And of all who have written of King Arthur the greatest is Lord Tennyson. No one who writes of the Round Table now can say just how much of the spirit of his stories he owes to him. It is easy for us to go back to the older books and to think that we are reading them and learning all that is in them for ourselves, but, whether we know it or not, we are always reading them by the light that he has given us.

If this book of mine can show you enough of the land of King Arthur to make you wish to see more of it with these other guides, it will open your way to an unbounded field of beauty and enjoyment.

THE COURT OF KING ARTHUR

CHAPTER I

HOW WE CAME TO LONDON

HELEN'S mother said that I might go, too, if I liked, and Helen said that I must go, too.

This Helen is a very young woman, with an extravagant fondness for stories. If you ever chance to meet her or anybody like her, never let her find out that you can tell stories or that you know anything about stories. That is, if your time is worth anything and if you do not enjoy telling stories for a very large part of it. Because, if you do let her know, you will never have any more peace. As for me, my time is not worth anything and I enjoy telling stories to any extent, so it doesn't matter.

But about this question of my going, too.

Helen and her mother had taken it into their
sensible heads to go abroad for the summer.
By listening carefully to all they said, whenever I got a chance, I could not find out that
they had any particular plans beyond that.
Neither of them had ever been abroad before,
and they seemed to have a sort of notion that
abroad meant Europe, and not any part of it,
but the whole of it.   I heard them talking now
and then of the Scotch Highlands, of the Al-
hambra, of the Rhine, of the Irish lakes, of the
Alps, and of seeing Naples and then dying,
and I felt sure that I should die before I saw
Naples if I tried to go to half the places where
they thought they were going.

That was why I did not care to say that I
would go till I knew just how much trouble
I was likely to get into.   It was not an easy
thing, by any means, for me to pretend that I
did not care much whether I went or not.
The memory of that glorious Rhine, with its
towering banks green and gray with vines and
castles, and of those calm, white-topped, giant
hills of Switzerland, so restful in their majesty,
stirred up longings in me that I should not
nave wished Helen and her mother to know,
till I had quite made up my mind to go with
them.   Still more than these, the grassy hillside pastures, the fields full of scarlet poppies,
the deep green hedges, and the smooth rivers

of England drew me toward them. They called to me and said: "Come to us again and be glad that you are here to see us and that we are here to be seen."

I can never think of these lands as real lands, where real people live and work, and are weary, and have real cares and troubles. They are all story lands, poet lands, fairy lands to me. I never saw them—and I am very glad of it— till I had known them long in books of old tales and in songs and in books of newer tales. And so they came to be to me, and they will always be, the countries of dim old kings, of knights with flashing arms and streaming plumes, of ladies who looked down on them from the walls of castles, of giants and of dwarfs; of stranger creatures still, of wizards and witches, of men who changed to wolves and women who changed to swans, of misty gods who rode on the storm winds, and heroes whom no sword could wound. Of course I know that the people there are real, and of course I have seen them working and playing and buying and selling and quarrelling together, but they did not look real—only like a part of the stories.

And not the least charm of these countries to me was that they were across the ocean and that we must make a voyage to reach them. For of all the people and the things that I love,

I love none, except a few of my friends, better than ships. I count ships among the people that I love, not among the things. Ships are noble, strong, beautiful, happy, living beings. It is absurd to think that they are anything else. When one of them has taken hundreds of us into herself and is bearing us from land to land, when she is driving along with us, finding her way alone through the darkness, with nothing but the stars above her and nothing but endless water all around—don't tell me that she is nothing but a dead machine! I have waked up in the night and felt the creature's great, hot heart beating, and I know. And when she is rushing on and on, by day and night, trying to cross the sea quicker than any other ship has ever crossed it; when she is trying to bring two great countries nearer together than they have ever been before, do you want me to believe that she does not know what she is doing, that only the captain on the bridge and the man at the wheel and the man at the engine know? Not a bit of it. I have stood at her prow and have seen her joy in her plunging and rising and sweeping through the waves; I have seen her dash the water into pearls by day and into glowing flame by night. Oh, she knows what she is doing better than anybody could tell her.

So you see I really wanted to go very much

indeed. And when I happened to overhear some little remark about the Parthenon I thought that the time had come to decide. "Could you give me any sort of notion," I asked, "whether you are really going to the Parthenon or to Ultima Thule, or where? Because it might help me to tell whether I can go with you."

"We don't know in the least where we are going," Helen's mother answered; "we only talk about what happens to come into our heads. If you will come with us, we will go just wherever you like."

"Wherever I like? Do you know what sort of promise you are making?"

"Why, it doesn't make any difference to us where we go," said Helen's mother, again, "and if you have any choice, we may as well go where you want to go as anywhere else. Only, of course, you must let me go to Paris. If you will say that I may go to Paris just when I like, you may plan everything else yourself."

"I say so, then, since you have given me this sudden authority."

"Then it is agreed, and you will go with us?"

"I will go with you."

I don't know why it is that Americans who go to England always make a straight line for London. There are plenty of other beautiful and interesting places that they ought to see

and that they mean to see.   Often, indeed, they
leave London again and go straight back on
their own tracks.   It seems strange, but it was
not for us to break through so firmly fixed a
custom.

And so we came to London.

CHAPTER II

THE NEW KING AT ST. PAUL'S

THERE are many good books that will tell you all sorts of useful and delightful things about London, if you care to know them. You will not find them here, for they have all been told much better than I could tell them. We saw as much of London as we could; it would take nothing less than a lifetime to see it all. It happened one day that we had been wandering around and about and up and down in St. Paul's Cathedral. We had been along the aisles and down into the crypt and had seen the tombs of great men till we were tired of them. We had climbed up to the Whispering Gallery and the Stone Gallery and the Golden Gallery, and we had gone higher still, till we were not sure whether we were in the ball or the cross. We have never been quite sure since. We were sure, when we came down, that we felt a trifle tired after so

much climbing, and that we wanted to rest for
a few minutes on one of the benches outside
the church, where we could watch the streams
of carriages and carts and omnibuses and people going past, and, nearer to us, the fountain
and the flocks of doves all about the walks.

"And now that we have nothing better to
do," I said, "do you want to hear a little history and then a story?"

"I don't care about the history," Helen answered.

"But you must hear the history before you
can hear the story. You can't have any cake
till you eat your bread."

"Then I will eat my bread. There isn't very
much of it, is there?"

"No, only a little. Very well, then. There
was a time, more than a thousand years ago,
when this London and this England were not
by any means the good places to live in that
they are now. There was no good queen up
the river at Windsor, and there was no castle
for her to live in if she had been there. Worse
than this, there was no Parliament at Westminster. Worst of all, there were plenty of
lords, who did little but misrule the people and
fight among themselves. There was no one
above the lords; no one could rule the whole
country, though there were many who would
have liked to try. There was a King of Scot-

land, and there was a King of Ireland, and there
was a King of North Wales, and a King of
Cornwall, and one of Cameliard, wherever that
was, and one of the Out Isles, wherever they
were. There were a dozen or twenty more
kings, perhaps, scattered about, one here and
one there, but they were no better and no more
powerful than the lords. Indeed, the more
power any of them had the worse it was for
their people; and of all England together
there was no king at all.

"There had been kings of England once,
but the last of them had been dead for a long
time and he had left nobody to take his place.
Uther Pendragon was far from being a good
man, but he was not a bad sort of king, for
those times. The most of the kings and lords
were robbers, and the people expected it, but
when there was one robber greater than all the
rest he kept the others down a little, and it was
better for the people than when there were a
hundred robbers, each one plundering them
for himself. That was the way after Uther
Pendragon died. Every lord tried to be a
greater thief than every other lord, and every
one of them, secretly or openly, hoped that he
might grow great enough to make himself king.

"There were not many cities then, and the
people lived in little towns and villages, far
away from one another, where the lords and

their armed men could do with them what they pleased. So they made the poor people work at building their castles. They gave them no pay and they left them no time to keep their shops or till their fields, so that while the men worked their wives and their children starved. Then they would take the land itself and drive the people away from it to die of hunger or to steal and be hanged for it. If they heard that any common man had saved a little money, they put him in a dungeon where there were snakes and toads, and kept him there till he promised to show them where he had hidden it. Then the lords fought with one another, and brought bands of armed men into one another's lands, and trampled down the fields of grain, and burned the houses, and killed the people. And perhaps that was the best thing for them.

"So the people loved to remember Uther Pendragon, and wished, but scarcely hoped, that there might be another king as good as he. They sat by their poor fires in the winter nights, and perhaps some of the old men told them how, long ago, the Romans came from far over the sea and over the land and conquered the country and kept it for many years. 'They were cruel fighters, the Romans,' the old men said, 'but they kept some kind of order in the land, and it was better than this.'

"Then they told how the heathen Saxons came, after the Romans had gone. Sometimes they drove the people out of their houses, and sometimes they made peace with the kings, who were strong men in those days. They were usually bad men, too, but it was better than this. And then the old men told of Uther Pendragon. 'He was the best of them all,' they said. 'Some of you younger men can remember him; it was not so many years ago that he died. But he left us no son to rule as he had ruled, and there is no hope now.' And they wiped their eyes with the backs of their hard hands, though it was long since there had been any such frivolous things as tears there.

"There were some of the lords, no doubt, who were not so bad as the others, but it was not easy in those days to be a good man and a lord at the same time. You see, if a lord happened to be a good man, he would not steal from the others, but they would all steal from him just the same as from anybody else. So he always lost as much as the others and never got so much back, and in that way he was likely to grow poor pretty fast.

"Yet there were a few such men. And so, in the bright summer days, as they worked together in the fields, the poor people would now and then talk a little more hopefully. They felt more cheerful in the summer, I suppose, because then they were only hungry, instead of hungry and cold both, as they were in the winter.

" ' There is old Sir Ector riding by, with his two sons,' one of the younger men would say; ' if all the lords were like them, it would be better for all of us.'

" 'Yes,' some old man would answer, 'Sir Ector was one of Uther Pendragon's men. The old King gave him all those lands that he has around London; he is rich enough; he does not need to steal from the poor.' The old men, you see, who remembered the better days, were the ones who were most hopeless and bitter.

" ' Does not need to steal from the poor!' one of the women would say; 'he would not steal. He is a good man, and his wife is a good woman. When my mother was sick last winter our house was so cold and damp that she would have died, but Sir Ector's wife heard about her and she let me bring her to the castle, and the servants took care of her till she got well.'

" 'Yes,' the old man might say again, 'and what happened then? When your own lord heard of it he went to Sir Ector and said that he must pay him money for taking one of his people off his land, and, when Sir Ector called his men and drove him away, your lord sent his men to burn your house for revenge. What good did it do you or your mother to save her life?'

"Nobody could answer such a question as this, but still somebody else would say that there might be better times if only such a man as Sir Ector could be King of England, and one of his sons after him. And the old man would growl again and say: 'Which of his sons? It would be Kay, because he is the older, and Kay is a harsh, surly boy; he would be as bad as any of these lords are now.'

"'Yet they say Kay is strong and brave,' one of the younger men would answer, 'and he is to be made a knight next Hallowmas. But I like his brother Arthur better. He is as kind and generous as his father. And I have seen him playing with the village boys, just as if he were not a lord's son, and he could run faster than any of them and throw a stone and shoot an arrow farther and straighter than any of them.'

"'What is the use to talk about them?' the old man would say at last. 'They can do nothing against these robbers that build their castles all over the land, and they do not try to do anything. And there is that old fool Merlin. Why does he never do anything for the people?'

"'How do you make out Merlin a fool? They say he knows more than any one else in the world, and he can do wonderful things by magic.'

"'That is just why I call him a fool. He can do wonderful things, and yet he never does anything. Is he not a fool, if he knows so much and could do so much for the people and for the country, and yet does nothing at all?'"

"Is this the story or the history?" Helen asked.

"This is the story."

"I thought it sounded more like a story. Where did the history leave off?"

"I am afraid I can't tell you exactly. You see, the history and the story are so mixed up together in the most of this that I have been telling you that it might not be quite safe to say that any of it was entirely history. But there is this strange thing about many of these old tales that I am just beginning to tell you: the people who like history better than stories generally think that they are all stories and nothing else, and the people who like stories better try to believe that there is a good deal of history in them. When you have heard them I am sure you will want to believe that they are all true. That is because you like stories better than history.

"But now for the story. It was this same Merlin—this old fool, who could do so much and did so little—who had scarcely thought of

anything all these long, terrible years but of
helping England and the poor people in it. He
was a strange man, this Merlin. He was an
old man, and people said that he knew everything that ever had been and everything that
ever should be. Nobody knew who his father
was. There was nothing so very wonderful
about that, but some said that he never had
any father, and there was something wonderful
about that. Others said that his father was
not a man, but a spirit of the air, and that that
was why he knew so much. He could take any
shape he chose, they said. Now and then somebody would tell how he had met a child or a
young man or a beggar, and how the child or
the young man or the beggar had told him of
strange things that were soon to happen, and
then had vanished. Then he knew that it was
Merlin, who had chosen to take some other
shape than his own, and always the things that
Merlin said proved to be true.

" Merlin had been the friend of Uther Pendragon. The people could remember wonderful things that he had done for the old King,
and that was why they thought it strange that
he did nothing now. But Merlin had his own
reasons for waiting. He knew what he had to
do when the time came. And now he knew
that the time had come. Just when another of
those cruel, cold, hungry winters was coming

upon the people, Merlin went to the Archbishop of Canterbury.

"The Archbishop of Canterbury was a wise
and good man. He was at the head of the
Church for all England, and he was the only
man who was at the head of anything for all
England. No doubt that was why Merlin went
to him. 'It is time,' said Merlin, 'to find a
king for England.'

"'Merlin,' the Archbishop answered, 'these
wicked lords are killing all the people and
spoiling all the land. What can we do? How
shall we find a king?'

"'It is you who must find him,' said Merlin.
'Will you do exactly what I tell you and not
ask me why?'

"People who know everything never like to
answer questions. It is most unfortunate, too.
The rest of the world might learn so much
from them.

"'Merlin,' said the Archbishop, 'some say
that you are the son of an evil spirit. Yet you
come into my church and you are not afraid of
the cross, or the holy water, or any of the holy
things. That is not like the son of an evil
spirit, and I have never known you to do anything but good. I will do what you tell me,
and if you do not wish me to know why, I will
not ask.'

"'Then,' said Merlin, 'send to all the great

lords of England and bid them come together in London at Christmas. Tell them that when they are met it shall be shown to them who is their rightful king.'

" As soon as Merlin had said this he was gone. The Archbishop did not see him go. He only looked at the place where Merlin had been and saw that there was nobody there. People who knew Merlin were used to little things like this, and they did not mind them much. Still the Archbishop felt that Merlin had told him a great deal less than he should like to know. Perhaps you would like to hear where Merlin went, and when you have heard you will know more about it than the Archbishop did. He travelled faster than the wind, and he went away up into the north of England to visit an old man named Bleys. Bleys was much older than Merlin himself, and he was very wise. It was said that he was Merlin's master when Merlin was a child. Why he needed a master I don't know, for Merlin knew more the day he was born than Bleys ever knew in his life. But now Bleys was writing a book, a sort of history of England, and he never wrote anything in it except just what Merlin told him. And when Merlin was missing, as he was pretty often, he was usually up there in the North, telling Bleys what to write in his book. I am sorry the book got lost, for it

might have settled a good many things that
have since been in doubt. Still it never would
have settled anything at all if it were as hard
to understand as a certain long prophecy of
Merlin's which did not get lost.

"But the Archbishop believed that whatever
Merlin told him to do must be right, so he sent
messengers to all the lords and told them to
come to London on Christmas to find out who
was to be king. Then there was a mighty stir
among the lords, you may be sure. Every one
of them, secretly or openly, wanted to be king,
and I suppose at least every other one secretly
thought that he might be. One thought that
the Archbishop would be his friend and would
choose him. Another thought that he could
bribe the rest and get them to choose him.
Another thought he could scare the people into
choosing him. Probably none of them felt so
completely puzzled about what was to happen
as the Archbishop himself.

"So when Christmas came all the lords met
in a church here in London. Some of the little
kings were there too. They were all ready to
cut one another's throat at a second's notice.
and they all looked very meekly and very
reverently at the Archbishop to see what he
was going to do first. Now, this story that I
am telling you is one that I have read in sev-
real books, but only one of them all says any-

thing about what church it was where the
lords met. That one, the one I like best of all,
says : 'The greatest church of London,
whether it were Paul's or not the French book
maketh no mention.' Now, if the good old
knight who wrote this book did not feel sure
' whether it were Paul's or not,' I shall take the
liberty of believing that it was Paul's. So I
tell you that they met here in this very church
where we are, and that it was just over there,
near where Powle's Cross was afterwards, that
they discovered such a wonderful thing.

" I know very well that the little book about
the Cathedral that we bought of the verger says
that 'In 610, Ethelbert, King of Kent, under-
took the building of the Cathedral of St. Paul.'
I know very well, too, that that was some hundred years or so after the time I am telling
you about, but that makes no difference to me.
There are two ways of believing things. You
may believe them with your head, or you may
believe them with your heart, and if you always like stories as well as you do now, you
will often find it pleasant to believe things with
your heart that you may not be quite able to
believe with your head. So I believe that it
was Paul's.

" When they were all met the Archbishop
had not the faintest notion of what he was to
do with them, but he thought that a good, safe

thing to do in any case would be to say mass. So he said mass. When the mass was over some of the lords, finding that nothing was likely to happen inside the church, came outside. And then, as they walked about, they found the wonderful thing that had appeared all of itself, just over there near the end of the choir. It was this: First there was a big square block of stone; then on the top of the stone there was an anvil; and then there was a sword stuck straight through the anvil and the stone. The sword had a beautiful jewelled hilt, and on it there were letters of gold which said: 'He who can draw this sword is the rightful King of England.'

"'Ah,' said every one of the lords to himself, 'now it will be very easy for me to show that I am to be King of England.'

"Some one had run to tell the Archbishop about the stone and the anvil and the sword, and he came to see them for himself. When he had looked at them he told the lords that all of them who liked might try to draw the sword. Of course every one of them wanted to try, and every one of them did try, but not one of them could move the sword. At that every one of them was greatly surprised and the Archbishop was greatly pleased, for there was not one among them who he thought was just the right man to be King of England.

" Then the Archbishop said : ' The true king is not here, but I know that he will come soon, and that we shall see him. So I bid you all to come here again on Twelfth Day, and then you may all try again to draw the sword, if you will, and any man in the whole land may try who will.'

" So he had a tent set over the stone and he chose ten good knights to guard it, night and day. I don't know why he thought it ought to be guarded. Anybody except the rightful King of England might as well try to steal the church as try to steal that sword. But I am only telling you just what happened.

" Well, to amuse themselves while they were waiting for Twelfth Day, the lords and the knights decided to have a tournament on New Year's Day, in the fields outside the town. Do you know what a tournament was ? It was a sham fight—a play battle. It was almost as dangerous as a real battle, for knights were often killed in tournaments. Indeed, I think the real difference between a battle and a tournament was that in a battle they usually fought about something, and in a tournament they usually fought about nothing.

" Now, among all the rest who had come to London, old Sir Ector had come, and he had brought Kay and Arthur with him. And on New Year's Day, as the three were riding to

the fields to see the tournament, Kay found
that he had forgotten to bring his sword. He
told Arthur to go back to the house where
they were staying and get it, and Arthur, like
a dutiful younger brother, went. But when he
got to the house it was locked up and deserted,
because everybody had gone to the tournament. Then Arthur remembered that he had
seen a sword sticking in an anvil in St. Paul's
Churchyard, and he at once thought that he
would go and get that for his brother Kay. I
can't think how a bright boy like Arthur could
have been in London for an hour without hearing that that sword was for nobody but the
King of England. But I am only telling you
what happened, and it seems he knew nothing about it. So Arthur, being the only per-
son in London who did not know that nobody
but the King could take that sword, just went
to the tent and took it and carried it to Kay.
The ten knights were not guarding it, for they
had all gone to the tournament too.

"But Kay knew all about the sword, you
may be sure. As soon as he saw it he took it
to his father and said: 'See; here is the
sword that was in the anvil; I am to be King
of England.'

"But Sir Ector knew his son Kay quite as well
as Kay knew the sword, and he ordered him to
come straight back to the church, and he told

Arthur to come, too. Then he said : ' Tell me, on your honor, Kay, how you got this sword.'

" And Kay, who, I think, was not such a bad fellow after all, answered : ' My brother Arthur brought it to me.'

" 'And how did you get it ? ' Sir Ector said to Arthur.

" 'Kay sent me for his sword,' Arthur answered, 'and I could not get it, because the house was locked, so I drew this sword out of the anvil to bring it to him instead.'

" ' Arthur,' said Sir Ector, 'if what you say is true, you are to be King of England.'

" ' I,' said Arthur, ' King of England ? Why ? '

" 'Because God has chosen you,' said Sir Ector. ' Now see if you can put the sword back in the anvil.'

" There was no hole in the anvil where the sword had come out, but as soon as Arthur touched the point to the iron it sank deep into it and into the stone. Then Sir Ector and Sir Kay both tried to draw it out, but they could not, and then Arthur drew it again as easily as he would have drawn a common sword from its sheath. And when he had done that Sir Ector and Sir Kay knelt down on the ground before him. ' Why do you kneel to me, my father and my brother ? ' said Arthur ; 'surely I am not better than you just because I can draw this sword.'

"'I am not your father,' Sir Ector answered, 'and I do not know who your father was. Surely he was a greater man than I, and surely you are better than we, for God has chosen you to be King of England.'

"'But I do not want to be King of England,' said Arthur, 'if I must lose you for my father. And my mother—is she not my mother?'

"'I do not know who your mother was,' Sir Ector answered, 'but my wife is not your mother. But, oh, Arthur, we have always loved you as if you were our own son—as much as we loved Kay, who is our own son. And so, Arthur, promise me now that when you are King you will do one thing that I ask of you.'

"'I will do all that you can ask of me, my father.'

"'Then promise me,' said Sir Ector, 'that when you are King you will make Kay seneschal of all your lands and of all your castles. And if he is ever rough or rude—for I know he is not like you, my own Arthur—promise me that you will forgive him, and remember that he was your foster-brother.'

"'Father,' said Arthur, 'if I am to be King, none but Kay shall ever be my seneschal as long as we both live.'

"Now Sir Ector hurried to tell the Arch-bishop what Arthur had done. 'Leave the sword where it was,' said the Archbishop, 'and say nothing about it till Twelfth Day. Come then, and Arthur shall draw the sword before all the people.'

"So on Twelfth Day the lords all came to St. Paul's again, and the Archbishop stood up before them and said: 'To-day it shall be shown to you who is to be your King. Swear, now, all of you, here before God and before me, His priest, that, whoever draws this sword, you will obey him, honor him, guard him, and be faithful to him as your true and only King.'

" And when they had all taken this oath the Archbishop said: 'Now let every one try to draw this sword who will.' And they all pulled and tugged at it, as they had done before, and not one of them could move it. Then the Archbishop led Arthur to the stone, and he drew out the sword and held it up before them all. And the Archbishop said: 'This is Arthur, your King.'

"The Archbishop thought that the lords would all kneel before the King at once, and swear again to be his true subjects, but not one of them moved. Then they began to mutter one to another; then they talked angrily and said: 'We cannot take this boy for our King, Who is he? Only old Sir Ector's son. Why should we obey him?'

"'He is not my son,' said Sir Ector; 'he is of a better blood than any of us.'

"'Of what blood, then?' they all asked.

"'I do not know,' said Sir Ector; 'but he has drawn the sword. Is not that enough?'

"'No,' they all cried again, 'he is nobody's son; he shall not be our King.'"

"Then one of them asked the Archbishop to wait till Candlemas, and to let them all try the sword again. And the Archbishop said that it should be so. And on Candlemas they all came back and tried again, and again none of them could draw the sword but Arthur. Still the lords said that Arthur should never be their King, and they said that they would try again at Easter. And when Easter came it was just as before, and they said again that they would wait till Pentecost. Then the Archbishop feared that some of the lords would try to do some harm to Arthur, so he put a guard around him, to be with him always. He chose knights whom he could trust for this guard. They were knights, the most of them, who had been Uther Pendragon's men, and had been faithful to him. Ulfius and Brastias were two of them. I tell you their names because I may have more to say about them some time.

"All this time nobody in London heard anything about Merlin. But I do not believe that he spent all these months in telling Bleys what to write in his book. I think that he was going about among the common people, talking with them, telling them about this Arthur, this new King whom they were to have, and urging them to come to London at Pentecost and help to choose him. Many of the people, I dare say, were willing enough, for they hated the cruel lords who ruled them, and they thought that any change must be good. But there were others who had suffered so much that they did not believe there could ever be good times any more. There were some, too, who feared their lords even more than they hated them, and with these Merlin had a harder task. 'I do not want any new king,' said one of these; 'my lord up there in the castle is good enough for me.' He did not know who Merlin was.

"'Your lord is good enough for you?' asked Merlin. 'Is he kind to you? Does he rule you well?'

"'He rules well enough,' the man said; 'I will not say anything or do anything against him.'

"'He rules well enough?' Merlin repeated. 'You saved a little money once, to use when you were old or sick; where is that money?'

"'I never saved any money,' the man answered.

"'What is that deep scar across your forehead?' Merlin asked.

"'I got it in a fight with clubs, when I was a boy,' the man answered.

"'You are telling me lies,' said Merlin. 'You did save some money. Your good lord heard of it and he sent his men to drag you up there to the castle. They put a strong cord around your head and tied it in a knot behind; they put a stick through the knot and twisted the cord with the stick and tightened it till it almost cut the top of your head off. It would have cut the top of your head off if you had not told them where you had buried your money. And you love this lord! Go and tell your lies to him; do not tell them to me. You hate him in your heart. You would like to murder him if you thought you would not be hanged for it. Will you come to London now and help to choose Arthur for your King?'

"The man had fallen on his knees. 'Yes, yes,' he cried; 'I know now that you are Merlin; all that you have said is true; I will do whatever you say.'

"'Then come to London at Pentecost.'

"There was an old man who told Merlin that a new king could do no good. 'He would be as bad as the rest; each of them is worse than the others.'

"'Would he be worse than the lord you have now?' Merlin asked.

"' No, he could not be worse than that. Do you know what this lord did ?'

"'Yes,' said Merlin, 'I know what he did, but you may tell me.'

"' He robbed me of everything I had,' said the old man, 'and then, when I had nothing else left, he said I must give my daughter to be married to one of his men who wanted her. He said he had a right to marry her to whom he pleased. I do not know. They have all the rights and we have no rights. I was away in the fields when they came to get her, but my son was here, and he knocked down the man who tried to touch his sister. For that they carried him to the castle and locked him in a dungeon. That was a year ago. I do not know whether he is alive now or not. I hope he is dead; it is better for him if he is.'

"Merlin made no answer to all this. He only said: 'You are an old man; do you remember Uther Pendragon?'

"'Remember him?' the other cried. 'Remember Uther Pendragon? Did I not fight for him in the last of all his battles? The King was sick and could not ride with his knights. We had no leader and the Saxons always drove us before them. We could not stand against them. Then it was told that we should never beat them till the King himself came to the battle. And they brought him in a litter

and carried him among his knights. He passed
close to me, and when I saw how pale he
looked I said to the man who stood next to
me : " The King is weak : we must be his
strength to-day." And he passed the word
along the line and all the men gripped their
bows harder. And when the King, lying there
almost dying, called out and cheered us on,
his knights fought like furies, and we all shot
our arrows farther and faster than we had ever
shot them before. And how the Saxons ran
before us ! Ran away, all of them—all but
those who were left lying on the field ! And
those three great leaders of theirs, Octa, and
Ebissa, and Ossa—they were left lying on the
field with the rest. Yes, I remember Uther
Pendragon.'

" The old man had got quite excited, but
Merlin looked at him sternly. 'When they
told you,' he said, 'that you would win the battle if the King came, did you believe it ? '

" ' No,' said the old man, ' none of us believed
it would make any difference, but when we saw
him and when ——'

" ' Yes, yes,' said Merlin, looking sterner still,
' and who was it whom you did not believe ?
Who was it that said that the King must come
to the battle ? '

" The old man stared at Merlin for an instant
in a startled way and then dropped his eyes

before his fierce look and trembled. 'Oh, I had forgotten, I had forgotten,' he cried; 'it was you.'

"'Yes,' said Merlin, 'it was I. You did not believe me then, just as you do not believe me now. But what I said then was true, and what I say now is true. I tell you that this Arthur will be a better king than Uther Pendragon. I will tell you more: your son, up there in the dungeon of the castle, is not dead. But it is a year since he saw the light of day, and they are starving him, besides. He will not live much longer if he stays there. Will you help us to choose the new King?'

"'I will do whatever you say.'

"'Then come to London at Pentecost.'

"And when Pentecost came they were all here at St. Paul's again. Over there by the end of the choir stood the Archbishop, beside the stone and the anvil and the sword. Close to him was Arthur. Around them were the lords, and all the rest of the ground about the church was filled with the common people. They had not come merely to look on this time. They were weary of the quarrels of the lords, and they were resolved — they, the common people — that this time they would have a king.

"And the lords all came, one at a time, and tugged at the sword again, and when they were all tired Arthur drew it out and held it up before them.

"Then they all said, as they had said before, that they would put off the choice and would try again. But the Archbishop said that there should be no more delay; and Sir Ector and Sir Kay and Sir Ulfius and Sir Brastias stood around Arthur and called upon the Archbishop to make him King.

"While they and the lords were wrangling about it two strange men came along the road to the outer edge of the crowd. They looked so strange and fierce that those who first saw them were frightened. They were covered with dust, as if they had travelled far on foot. Their clothes were torn, their hair hung tangled about their faces, and they stared around them with wild, eager eyes. Some of the people thought that they were madmen and tried to get out of their path. But one of them cried: 'Where is this new King? We want to see him!'

"'There is no king yet,' somebody answered; 'be still; the Archbishop is going to speak.'

"But the man with the wild eyes would not be still. 'What do we care for the Archbishop?' he cried. 'We want a king. We have come from the seashore, down beyond the mouth of the river. Two days ago a ship full of pirates came there. They burned our houses and carried away our wives to sell for slaves, and our children—oh, I cannot think of what they did with the children! We could not help them, there were so many of the pirates. And they went away in their ship and left us with the ashes of our houses. But we had heard that you up here in London were choosing a new king. They told us that there had been a miracle to show who was the King. So we came to see him. We want to tell him what the pirates do to his people. We want to know if he can protect them better than these little lords. Where is he? If he can, we are for him.'

" ' There he is,' said some one, pointing, ' there beside the Archbishop ; the one with the sword in his hand—Arthur.'

" ' What, the boy who stands there so still and looks so pale? Well, he may be good and brave for all that. We have seen brave men turn pale, down there by the sea. What are they quarrelling about? Arthur, did you call him? Is he the one that did the miracle? Then we want him for our King ! Shout with us, all of you, and say that we will have him and that we will kill anybody who says he shall not be King ! I can shoot an arrow straight to any mark, and I will shoot all the arrows he will give me for this Arthur if he will be a real King and protect his people.'

" The men from the sea were so much excited, and they had such good reason to be, that those around them began to get excited, too. Then those farther off caught up the cry and in a moment all the people were shouting that Arthur should be King and that nobody should put him off any longer. But the lords, for one last time, cried out: 'We will try again; put the sword back in the anvil.' And then the Archbishop raised his hands and silenced them all, and said to Arthur, so that all could hear: 'Do not put the sword back; it is yours now; keep it, guard your people with it, and drive out their enemies. And now follow me.'

" Then he took Arthur by the hand and led him into the church and up the steps of the altar, where Arthur laid the sword. And the lords came in and the people followed them and filled the church, and still there was a great crowd outside, where the people pushed and struggled to get near the doors and called to those within to tell them what was done.

" When there was silence again the Archbishop said: 'My lords and people; here before this altar, all last night, Arthur watched his arms. He is ready now to be made a knight.' Then Arthur knelt before him and the Archbishop said: 'Do you swear to me

that you will love God and keep His laws;
that you will be always loyal and upright; that
the good and brave deeds you do shall be your
glory, and that you will do none for other glory
or for gain? Do you swear that you will be
faithful, gentle, and merciful; that you will
ever fight for the right of the poor and the
weak, and that you will fear shame more than
death?'

"And Arthur answered: 'I swear it.'

"The Archbishop took the sword from the
altar and touched Arthur's neck with the blade.
'Rise, Sir Arthur,' he said, 'and may God make
you a good knight.' Then he fastened the
sword upon Arthur's side.

"And now the Archbishop made all the lords
take again the oath, that they had kept so badly
since Twelfth Day, that they would be faithful
to the King and would obey him, honor him, and
guard him. And the lords, seeing that it was
of no use to do anything else, took the oath.

"Then the Archbishop said to Arthur again:
'Do you swear that you will keep and guard
your people from their enemies, as God shall
help you; that you will strive for peace and
justice in your land; that you will rule poor
and rich alike, and that you will give right to
all? Do you swear that you will be in all
things a true King to your people and a true
servant to the King of Kings?'

" And Arthur said : ' I swear it.'

" Then at last the Archbishop set the crown upon his head, and the people in the church shouted, and the people outside caught up the shout, and it rang for the first time, ' Long live King Arthur ! ' that shout that was to ring so many times and so long and never quite die away.

" And when it was all over and they came out into the churchyard, the stone and the anvil were gone."

CHAPTER III

THE ROUND TABLE

JUST what I said about London I will say again about the beautiful places in the Midlands of England. The books will tell you a great deal that is pleasant and useful of Oxford, with its spires and domes and towers; of Kenilworth, with its fine old ruined castle walls; of Warwick, with its fine old castle walls that are not ruined; of Stratford-on-Avon, where everybody talks about Shakespeare all day and dreams about Shakespeare all night; of Worcester, where they make cups and saucers and gloves and sauce. But if we leave all these behind and I try to tell you something about Caerleon-upon-Usk, perhaps I may not do it in quite the same way as the books.

I think very few people go to Caerleon-upon-Usk. The ticket-seller at the railway station in Newport looked surprised when we told him we wanted to go there. Still, he made no

objection. The one or two people about the
station at Caerleon-upon-Usk looked surprised
when we got off the train there. But they
asked no questions. The three or four whom
we met as we walked up the street looked surprised to see us. I had been told that to find
King Arthur's Round Table we must walk for a
few minutes along the road opposite the museum. The museum had columns on its front
that made it look as if it belonged to a Greek
town, instead of an English one, but the ram-
bling church, with the square tower, close by it,
looked English enough. It was not far to a
broad green field, with a low mound in the
middle of it, covered with grass like the rest.
This mound was in the form of a ring, with
a hollow in the middle and a gap at one side
for an entrance. Some children were playing
in the hollow. At one side of the field there
was a low stone wall, and in the middle of it
a gate, with a pointed arch of the same kind
of stone above it. The wall came only a little
way up the sides of the arch, and in the arch
itself there was just enough stone to hold together. It all looked very old. A little boy
sat on the stile that we had to cross to get
into the field, and when we spoke to him he
was more surprised than any of the other
people we had met. "Is this what they call
King Arthur's Round Table?" I asked.

"Yes, sir," he said; "and they call it the dingle."

"The dingle?"

"Yes, sir, they say it's that."

"But you have heard people call it King Arthur's Round Table, have you?"

"Yes, sir, I've heard that, too."

"What is that arch for?" I said, pointing across to the gateway in the wall.

"I don't know, sir."

"How old is it?"

"I don't know, sir; it's thirteen years old, anyway."

I was the one who was surprised at this. "Ah, is it?" I said; "it looks as much as a hundred. You never heard anybody say how old it was?"

"No, sir; it was there before I was born, and I'm eleven."

We gave the boy two or three pennies, and he hurried off to find some other boys and show them how much money there was in the world. I wondered, as we walked across the field and sat down on the mound, if King Arthur, with all the castles, and towers, and treasures that were his once here at Caerleon, ever felt as rich as this boy.

"For it was here," I said, "that Arthur lived, after they made him King, more than anywhere else, except at Camelot. Here he fought battles; here many times he held his court, with his knights around him; from here the knights rode away to find adventures; back here they came to tell their stories to the King and the Queen; and here now, they say, down under the ground, just under this very spot where we sit, in a great hall, with high pillars and arches that hold up this green field, King Arthur sits sleeping, with all his knights around him. The knights are asleep and their horses are all there beside them, asleep too. They wear their armor and their swords, and their spears are ready. And some time, they say, when the people of England are in great need, King Arthur and his knights will awake and will come and save the people, just as Arthur saved them before, so many hundred years ago. You see this is a very pretty story, but I am sorry to say that I cannot quite believe it."

"But you asked the boy," said Helen, "if that was King Arthur's Round Table, and he said it was; but I don't see any table."

"Neither do I, but what they call the Round Table is this very mound that we are sitting on."

"But this isn't a table," Helen insisted; "it looks more like a place for a circus."

"You are such a horribly clever child," I said, "that there is really no doing anything with you. That is probably just what it is, or was—a place for a circus. Long before Arthur's time the Romans held Caerleon. It was one of the greatest cities of all England then. And the Romans were always about as fond of circuses as the boys and girls in New York are now, so I have no doubt that they had one here, and that this is it. Still, King Arthur certainly lived at Caerleon and he certainly had a wonderful Round Table. Arthur must have been pleasanter for the people to remember, I suppose, than the Romans, and so, when they had forgotten all about what this mound really was, they began to call it the Round Table, and you see they call it so still.

"I have no doubt that it really was here at Caerleon that Merlin made the Round Table, for it was Merlin who made it. But it did not always stay here. This great pile of earth looks as if it would be rather hard to move, yet Arthur and his knights sat at the Round Table, sometimes here, sometimes at Camelot or Westminster, and once, the stories say, in Rome. It must have been rather a big and heavy affair, whatever it was, for there were places around it for a hundred and fifty knights. But one of the old stories says that, by the magic that Merlin put into it, it could be folded up and carried about, as easily as the cloth of an ordinary table. And that was not all of the magic. Merlin made the Round Table for Uther Pen-

dragon, who used to live here at Caerleon, too.
And Merlin made seats around it for the
knights, and when they were done he said to
Uther : 'All these seats you may fill with your
knights, except this one next your own. This
is the Siege Perilous. Nobody must ever sit
here except the best knight of all the world,
and he will not come to sit here till long after
you are dead.'

"Now, it was a strange thing that people usually did just about what Merlin told them as
long as he was looking. But when he went
away for a little while they began to find that
they never believed much of what he said, and
that they themselves knew quite as much as he.
And so, once, when Merlin was away, King
Uther's knights decided that it was all nonsense
about the Siege Perilous and the best knight of
all the world. The seat looked just like the
others, they said, and it was none too good for
any of them. Then one of them said that he
would sit in it himself, just to show that he
could. And he did sit in it, and that was the
last that was ever seen of him. All the rest
were watching, and they saw him sit down, and
then they saw that the seat was just as empty
as it was before. Nobody could see where he
went or what had become of him. Only there
was the empty seat, and the knight never came
back to tell where he had been. It was a long

time before anybody sat in the Siege Perilous again.

"After Uther Pendragon's time a certain king named Leodogran had the Round Table. He was King of Cameliard. I don't know what or where Cameliard was, but I have a dim sort of notion that it was somewhere far up in the North. I don't know, either, how King Leodogran got the Round Table. But he had it, and he kept it till Arthur—but that is getting ahead of the story.

"It was here to Caerleon that Arthur came, after he had been crowned at St. Paul's, and after he had put things straight around London and had arranged affairs so that they could go on a little better than they had been going before. And the Round Table was not here then. And here he invited all the great lords and all the little kings to a feast. But when the guests were all here he found that the kings had not come to eat and drink with him and to talk with him of what was best for the country, as he had thought they would, but to fight and to try to kill him.

"They made a great camp around the castle that stood not far from where we are sitting, and Arthur and his men went out and attacked them and drove them back. Many of the lords and knights were true to their promise now, and were on Arthur's side, and so were all the com-

mon people, except some that were under one
or another of the little kings and had to fight
for them, whether they liked it or not. Yet
Merlin thought it was not safe to try any great
battle yet, so he said to Arthur: 'Over in
France there are two good kings. They are
brothers, Ban and Bors. They are strong,
brave, and true men, but now another king,
Claudas, is making war upon them, and he is
so powerful that, strong and brave as they are,
they need help against him. Send word to
them that, if they will come to England and
help you against your enemies, you will go
back to France with them and fight against
King Claudas.'

"This seemed a good plan, and whether it
had seemed good or not Arthur would have
done whatever Merlin advised. So Merlin
himself went over to the two kings and told
them how Arthur had been made King of England, and how he was surely to be a greater
King than Uther Pendragon, and what a good
friend Arthur would always be to them, if they
would help him now. Then Merlin came back,
in less time than it would have taken anybody
else to go half-way to France, and told Arthur
that Ban and Bors would come.

"And when they came Merlin said that it
would be better to hide them and their knights
in the woods and let Arthur and his knights

fight with the kings alone for a while. That would make the enemy bolder, when they saw only a few coming against them, and would lead them on to the fight, and then King Ban and King Bors could come out of the woods and fall upon them. I don't know enough about battles myself to be quite certain whether this would do any good or not, but Merlin was always fond of surprises, and of course they did what Merlin said. He told Arthur, too, not to use the sword that he drew out of the stone till he got into the very thickest of the fight and really needed it.

" And the kings were all good fighters, and they had brave knights with them, and there were so many of them that when they saw the few knights of Arthur before them they thought that they could easily have the battle their own way. And so, indeed, it did look, for when their great crowd of horses and of men, with lances down, came rushing on toward the little band that Arthur had, it looked as if it could never stand against them. But if Arthur's knights were few they were as good as any in the world. There were Sir Ulfius and Sir Brastias and old Sir Ector, who had been Uther's men, and there were Sir Kay and Sir Lucan, King Arthur's butler, and many more who would be true to him as long as they lived. And if for one moment Arthur himself thought that his foes were too many and too strong for him, his next thought was : ' It is for my people ; they have suffered wrong from these men too long and too much, and they shall suffer it no more.'

"And he and his knights charged with their spears into the midst of their enemies. And after the spears were broken they drew their swords and struck to right and left. And when he saw his enemies all around him Arthur drew his sword that he took from the stone, and the good old fellows who wrote these stories hundreds of years ago say that it shone with a light like thirty torches. ' Look at him,' said one of the old knights to another, ' he fights as if he were Uther come back again.'

" ' No,' the other answered, 'he fights better than Uther ever did.'

" The rebel kings were beginning to find it out, too, old soldiers as they were. They thought that Merlin must be helping with his magic, but he was not ; it was only Arthur's own hard fighting. A strong young arm, with something good to fight for, is a bad thing to fight against, even for men who are older and better trained. And when Ban and Bors burst out of the woods, with all their men, and fell upon the enemy too, they simply turned and ran, those of them who could run. And still the blood of Arthur's men was up and they felt that they had not had half fighting enough, when Merlin called to them all to come back, for the rebel kings were beaten and there was no more to do.

"But in those dear old days nobody ever suffered long for want of a good fight. And so, almost before Arthur had done thanking Ban and Bors for the help they had given him, a messenger came to him from King Leodogran, of Cameliard. And this messenger said that a giant named Ryence, who was King of North Wales, was coming against Leodogran with a great army. He had sent to Leodogran to say that he had a mantle trimmed with kings' beards and he wanted Leodogran's beard to go with the rest. Leodogran must send him his beard or he would come and take it for himself, and then he would kill him and destroy everything in his country. Now Leodogran, the messenger said, did not like the notion at all of having to give his beard to another king to trim his clothes with, but he never in the world could fight Ryence alone and he begged Arthur to come and help him. When this message had been given Arthur looked around upon his knights. They were all still and all leaning forward to hear his answer, and the eyes of every one of them seemed to say to him 'Let us go.' And Ar-

thur looked at Ban and Bors, and the look in
their faces said 'We will go too.' And he
looked at Merlin and Merlin nodded, and Arthur said: 'Tell your King that I will come,
I and my friends, King Ban and King Bors.'

"So, as soon as they could make ready, they
all marched away up into the North. And one
evening, just as the sun was setting, they came
to the city of King Leodogran, and the gate
opened to let them in. And Arthur, riding at
the head of his knights, looked through the gate-
way; and all along the street, before the houses
and at the windows, there were lines of faces,
half pale with fear, half flushed with hope. For
the people seemed scarcely to know whether
the gate was opened for their friends or for
their foes; whether these long lines of horsemen, these bright armors, and these banners
brought them life or death. The King's castle
was just inside the wall of the town, and on
the battlement stood a crowd of ladies to see
the three kings and their knights go by.

"Arthur looked up at them and one among
them all caught his eye. The low sun was behind
her, so that he could not see her face well, but it
was young and he thought that it was the most
beautiful he had ever seen. Her hair was the
color of gold and it fell down upon her shoulders, and there were light waves of it all about
her head, and the low sun shone through it and

made it look to Arthur like the halo of a saint.
And he saw no more of the many frightened
and hopeful faces and none of the other ladies
on the battlement, but only that one face.
'Who is she?' he said to Merlin, who rode by
his side.

"And the wise old Merlin knew just where
Arthur was looking, and he answered: 'She is
the King's daughter, the Princess Guinevere.'

"They turned an angle of the castle wall and
she was gone. Arthur saw the anxious faces in
the street again. But he saw them dimly, for
still that one face was before his eyes, the face
darkened, with the sun behind it, but around it
the halo of the saint. He did not know whether
she had seen him or not.

"The next day Ryence and his army were
before the town, and the four kings, Arthur and
Ban and Bors and Leodogran, with all their
knights, went out against them. Every one had
all the fighting he wanted that day, for Ryence
had more men than the other four kings put together, and he thought he saw a chance to get
four beards for his mantle, instead of one. Besides that, Ryence was more than twice as tall
as an ordinary man and some of his knights
were giants too. They were not easy fellows
to fight against.

"Merlin carried Arthur's banner, and it was
a very wonderful banner, that he had made

himself. It had a dragon on it breathing **fire**
out of its mouth. There was nothing strange
about that, of course, and sometimes people
looked at it and saw nothing about it any more
wonderful than any other banner. But in the
crowd that stood in the streets to see them all
go out through the gate to the battle there was
a woman who held up a child to see the horses
and the armors. 'Oh, look at the banner!' the
child cried; 'what is it doing?'

"'Yes,' the woman said, 'a pretty banner,
isn't it?' She had seen it a minute before and
now she was looking at the bright, painted
shields and the plumes on the helmets.

"'But look at it,' the child cried again; 'it's
all on fire.'

"The woman looked at it again and then she
almost dropped the child. 'Look, look,' she whispered to another woman who stood next to her;
'the dragon on the banner is breathing real fire!'

"And so it was; instead of the little spots of
gold that they had seen before, real sparks
floated from the jaws of the dragon on the banner and went out in the air just above it. The
whisper the woman had started grew and ran
all through the crowd and everybody looked at
the banner. 'It is Merlin carrying it,' said an
old man; 'we may beat them yet, with Merlin
on our side.'

"And then the battle began, and the fiercer it

grew the more the dragon on the banner spouted fire. Always Merlin kept the banner beside Arthur, and so always it was in the thickest part of the fight. And when Arthur's men saw that great torch blazing higher and brighter, it made them feel that their side was growing stronger; and when the men of Ryence saw it, they feared more and more, because it made them feel that some power they did not understand was against them.

"And Arthur fought that day as he had never fought before. He had come because he wanted to help the good King Leodogran against the cruel tyrant Ryence, but now he had something more to fight for. He looked straight at the helmet that he charged against with his spear, or at the shield that he struck with his sword, or he glanced sharply around him, that no enemy might come upon him unawares, but always, beyond the charging helmet and above the shield and through all the dust of the battle he saw that face that he had seen last night upon the castle wall. And always when he saw it plainest, he struck harder with his spear or sword, and every one of his enemies went down before him. He was not the first man or the last who ever struck harder because he saw such a face as that always before him.

"And all day the battle went on, the crowds

of fighting men and horses now surging up
close to the city wall, now drifting away from
it across the plain, and all the women and the
children and the old men who could find
places stood on the wall to watch. And once
they saw a sight that made them all tremble and
turn pale. For Ryence and half a dozen of his
giant knights charged down upon King Leodogran and threw him from his horse and
seized him and were dragging him away as
their prisoner. And Arthur was resting for
a moment, when Merlin cried out to him : 'Do
not stop now; go on; there is more work for
you ; look!'

"And Arthur looked and saw Leodogran
and Ryence and the rest. But he saw more
than that, for there, upon the castle rampart,
looking out over the city wall, she stood again
—the Princess Guinevere. She saw her father,
and her face was full of terror and she tried to
turn away, but she could not, and still she
gazed at him and at the giants who were dragging him away. Just for an instant Arthur
looked at her and thought: 'This time she
shall see me.' Then he spurred his horse and
charged straight against King Ryence. And
Merlin kept by his side, and the flame from the
mouth of the dragon on his banner was higher and fiercer than it had ever been before.
'What did I say to you in that other battle?'

said one of Arthur's knights to another. 'Did Uther ever fight like that?' And before the other could answer they both wheeled their horses and dropped the points of their spears and charged against two of the knights of Ryence and threw them from their saddles. Their armors clashed as the horses of Arthur's knights struck them with their hoofs, and they dashed on against more of their enemies.

"And Arthur and Ryence were fighting the most terrible fight of all that day. For Ryence was big and strong, and Arthur, thinking of the eyes that were on him, felt himself grow bigger and stronger than Ryence. The giant had a beautiful, bright, sharp sword. It was said that Vulcan had made it for Hercules and that Ryence was his descendant. And Arthur thought : 'If I could only win that sword, it would be the finest thing that I could carry off this field of battle. And as they fought Ryence struck a savage blow at Arthur and hit his shield and cut it half in two ; and there his sword stuck and he could not draw it out. Then Arthur gave Ryence a deep wound, and he turned and fled and left his sword sticking in Arthur's shield.

"There was none of Ryence's men left in that place now. Arthur found a horse that had belonged to one of them and brought it to King Leodogran and helped him to mount.

Next he drew the sword of Ryence out of his
shield, and then he and his knights followed
Ryence and his men, who were all fleeing now.
They followed them till they were all broken
up and scattered, and then they knew that the
battle was won and they turned to go back to
the town. The gate was opened for them and
they all passed in, Arthur and Merlin and Leodogran and Ban and Bors and all their knights;
and the people crowded to the gate to meet
them and filled the streets and cheered and
wept and laughed, and the dragon on Merlin's
banner breathed a stream of fire high up into
the air, above the very towers of the castle.

"That night Leodogran made a feast in his
castle hall. And there sat the four kings and
all the best of their knights and Merlin. And
the Princess Guinevere served them, as prin-
cesses did in those days. But there were two
in the hall who ate and drank nothing. One of
them was Arthur. After all the work and the
heat of that day he could not eat. He only sat
and watched the Princess, as she moved about
the hall. He did not think that the others
might be watching him, and I believe that all
that he thought was: 'I must look well at her
now, for if I leave this place to-morrow I may
never see her again.'

"I suppose Merlin knew all this, because he
knew everything, but of all the rest only one

was watching Arthur. That was Leodogran, and when he saw that Arthur's eyes followed Guinevere everywhere she went, he too could not eat. And his thought was: ' He is as brave as my child is beautiful.' Then the Princess herself came and knelt before Arthur and offered him a gold cup full of wine and said: ' My Lord, drink this; why should you be afraid to eat and drink? You are not afraid to fight.'

"And Arthur gazed at her still, and when he tried to answer her he scarcely knew what he said, but it seemed to him that it had been unmannerly in him to sit there without eating as he had, and he took the wine and said: 'I thank you, and I will repay you if I ever have the power.'

" ' You have done more for me already, my Lord,' she said, 'than I can ever deserve of you. You have saved my father's country and his people and you saved my father's life too. I saw you and I saw it all, there before the gate, and you might have lost your own life.'

"Do you think that Arthur ate or drank any more after that? But Leodogran tried to laugh and to cheer on the others and to make the night a happy one, but still his eyes were on those two and still his one thought was ' He is as brave as my child is beautiful.'

" The next day Arthur and Ban and Bors,

with all their knights, began their march home, for Merlin said : ' It is time for you to fight King Claudas, in France.' They came to Camelot, where Arthur had another castle, even greater and more beautiful than the one here at Caerleon. And there, as they entered the hall of the castle, four young men came to meet them and knelt before Arthur. ' My Lord,' said one of them, ' I am Gawain, and these two are my brothers, Gaheris and Agravain; we are the sons of King Lot, and this other is Uwain, our cousin, the son of King Urien. We have come to be your men. Our father, King Lot, fought against you with the other kings, but we have tried to make him your friend, and he has promised us that he will be so now and will be faithful to you, if you will be his friend and will forgive him.'

" Arthur looked around upon his knights. They were all silent, and two or three of them shook their heads. Then he looked again at the young men before him. They had fresh, glowing young faces and big bodies and strong arms, and their bright young eyes looked eagerly into his for their answer. He turned to his knights once more. ' Old friends,' he said, ' your hearts are all true to me, I know, as true to me as they were to Uther when you were his men. You are tried and brave and faithful, but how long can I depend on you? I must have men like these to help me build up my kingdom. They are such as I am myself. I will forgive King Lot; we have enemies enough; we need friends.'

"Arthur had not spoken to Merlin, though he stood close at his side—had not looked at him. But now Merlin whispered: 'Oh, my King, it is only a little while longer that I can be with you, but now when the time comes I can leave you and you will not need me; you are the King.'

"'My Lord,' said Gawain, 'will you make us knights?'

"And Arthur drew his sword and touched the shoulder of each of them with it and said: 'Rise, Sir Gawain, Sir Gaheris, Sir Agravain, and Sir Uwain, and may God make you good knights.'

"Then they all marched on again and crossed over into France and fought with King Claudas, the enemy of Ban and Bors. And when they had beaten him and driven him back to his own country, Arthur said to the brother kings: 'We do not need each other any more. You have helped me more than I could help you, for I needed help more than you. So I have not repaid you for all that you have done. I must go back now to my own people, but if I can ever do more than I have done to show you how grateful I am, tell me of it, now or when the time comes, and nothing will please me so much as helping you.'

"Bors answered first and said : 'One thing I have thought already that I would ask of you. We have never seen such a court before as that you keep. Your knights are the bravest we have ever found. You are always generous and just to them, and to all your people. In their battles and dangers you are one of them. They love you as no other men in the world love their king. These things will soon be told all through the world, and then the bravest and noblest everywhere will want to come to you and be your knights. Now this is what I ask : I have a son whose name is Bors, like mine. When he is old enough I wish that he might be made a knight by you and live at your court, for there he will learn all that is truest and noblest and gentlest and best for a good knight to know.'

"'Let him come,' said Arthur, 'but again the favor and the help will be to me, not to you.' And then he looked at King Ban.

"'I cannot ask anything,' said Ban. 'My brother has asked the best gift of you that any king could ask. I would ask the same, but my son is lost—my Galahad. Shall I tell you how ? Once this same Claudas came against my castle with such a force that I could not resist him. To save my wife and my child I took them and one servant with me and we left the castle at night. No one saw us till we had gone far through the woods. Then we met two of Claudas's knights and I and my servant went forward to fight with them. I fell and the Queen thought that I was wounded. She put the child down on the ground and ran to help me. When she saw that I was not hurt she went back to find the child. A woman sat under a tree, holding him in her arms. She arose when the Queen came near her, went to the edge of a lake that was near, and jumped in with the child. Both of them sank out of sight and we have never seen our child since then. Some have told us that it was the Lady of the Lake who took him. They say that he is not dead, but that she is still keeping him with her and is teaching him all that a young knight ought to know. It may be true, but I do not hope to see him again. My brother has asked of you the best of gifts for his son, but I can ask nothing for Galahad.'

" When Ban had told this story no one spoke at first, and then Merlin said : ' My lord, the best knight who will ever come to your court will be Galahad.'

" Arthur and Ban both looked at him with the same question in their eyes : ' Then he was not drowned, and he will come ! ' But Merlin would say no more. He only repeated : ' The

best knight who will ever come to your court
will be Galahad.'

"And Arthur said to Ban: 'If your son
lives and comes to me, I shall welcome him
gladly for your sake, and it will make me glad-
dest of all if my best knight hereafter shall
remind me always of you, who are my best
friend now.'

"It was not long after Arthur had come
back to England when he began to find himself
disturbed in a new way. He said to Merlin
one day: 'My knights and my lords keep com-
plaining to me. They say it is not right that
such a court as mine should have only a king
at the head of it, and that it ought to have a
queen, too.'

"Now of course I don't say that it was
really the knights and the lords who were most
anxious about this: I only say that that was
what Arthur told Merlin. You know very
well who in all that court probably thought
most about a queen. If Arthur thought that
he could deceive such persons as you and Merlin and I, he was very much mistaken.

"But Merlin looked very serious and asked
Arthur, just if he did not know what was
coming, if he had thought of anybody for his
queen.

"'Yes,' said Arthur, 'Guinevere, the daughter of King Leodogran.'

" Merlin did not look so glad as Arthur thought he ought to look. It must be very uncomfortable, I think, to know as much as Merlin knew. 'Will you go to her father,' Arthur went on, 'and ask him to give her to me, and will you bring her back with you to Camelot?'

" Merlin still looked grave and sad, but he only said: 'Yes, I will go.'

" And, so, not many days after, a splendid procession came through the gate of Camelot and up the street to the castle of the King. There were many knights of King Arthur and many knights of King Leodogra.., all with their gayest armor and their brightest shields and their tallest plumes, and in the midst of them all rode King Arthur himself and the Princess Guinevere, for he and his knights had gone out to meet her. And Merlin rode before them and carried his banner, with the fire-breathing dragon.

" So Guinevere was married to Arthur in the Church of St. Stephen, at Camelot. And when they came from the church to the great hall of the castle they saw a strange sight. For there, in the middle of the hall, stood that wonderful Round Table that Merlin had made for Uther Pendragon so long ago. All around it were the seats for the knights, and there was one seat, higher and wider than the rest, for the King. It had a canopy of silk above it and great golden dragons all around, with jewelled eyes, that shone like fire.

"Then Merlin said: 'King Arthur, this is the wedding-gift that King Leodogran has sent to you. It was the Round Table of Uther, but now forever all the world shall know it as the Round Table of Arthur. Here are seats for a hundred and fifty knights. King Leodogran has sent you a hundred knights; the other seats you must fill yourself, all but this one next your own. This is the Siege Perilous. While you live and reign the greatest knights of the world shall sit at this table, but in the Siege Perilous no one shall sit till the one best knight of all the world comes to take it.'

"Then, as they looked at the seats, they saw that the name of some knight was in each one of them, in letters of gold. And always after that, when any new knight was to sit at the Round Table, his name came of itself in letters of gold in the seat that he was to have. And now Merlin made them all take their places and hold up their swords, with their cross-shaped hilts high above their heads, and take the oath of the Knights of the Round Table. 'Do you swear,' he said, 'that you will help the King to guard his people and to keep peace and justice in his land; that you will be faithful to your fellows; that you will do right to poor and rich alike? Do you swear that in all things you will be true and loyal to God and to the King?'

"And every one of them said: 'I swear it.'

"And there were the hundred knights that Leodogran had sent, and there were Gawain and Uwain and Gaheris and Agravain and Ector and Kay and Lucan and Ulfius and Brastias and many more of Arthur's best knights. And as long as Arthur lived, to be a knight of the Round Table was the greatest honor that a knight could have. And knights and lords and even kings came from other countries to sit at that table. And some who might have been kings in their own countries stayed here always to be Arthur's knights. For they thought it was a greater thing to be called a knight of that Round Table than to be called a king in another land; and so it was."

"And you don't believe, after all," Helen asked, "that this is really the Round Table, here where we are sitting?"

"No," I said; "just while we sit here we can make believe that we believe that it is, but I don't believe it really."

CHAPTER IV

NOT GALAHAD, BUT LANCELOT

WE left the field of the Round Table and walked back toward the museum, and then down to the river and across the bridge and back. As we looked away down the Usk we wondered if the view was much changed from the one that Arthur and Guinevere and Merlin used to see. A pretty view it was, with hills rising from the river in gentle slopes and all covered with green woods. It would have been prettier still if the water had looked clearer and if there had been less mud on the banks.

"There is one little story that I think you ought to hear," I said, "before I tell you any others, though it has nothing to do with Caerleon. It belongs to Camelot, where you know I told you King Arthur lived even more of the time than here."

"Are we going to Camelot, too? ' Helen asked.

" I am not quite sure about that," I said.
" We will try to. The trouble is that there is
no such place as Camelot now, or, at any rate,
no such city, and nobody knows just where it
was. When nobody knows, of course anybody
has a right to guess. So one says that Camelot was here and another says that it was there.
We will do our best to find it, but the worst
of it will be that we shall never really know
whether we have found it or not.

" Well, wherever it was, it was a beautiful
city, with high walls around it and great gates
in them, and with fine houses and splendid
churches. And Arthur had a castle there even
greater and more beautiful than the one here
at Caerleon. And once the ladies of the castle
stood on the ramparts, just as they had stood
on those of the castle of King Leodogran when
Arthur came to Cameliard, and looked down
to see the people who passed. And they saw
a strange little procession coming slowly along
the road toward the castle. It was very different
from that other procession, when Arthur and
Ban and Bors and their knights marched into
the city up in the North to save the old King
and his people. There were knights here, too,
and squires, and they rode handsome horses
and wore rich clothes. And two of the
squires led the most beautiful horse of all.
It was pure white, with flowing mane and tail

and great dark, flashing eyes. On its back it carried an armor that gleamed in the sun as if it were made all of silver, and a shield. Another squire carried a shining helmet, that matched the armor, and another carried a sword in a scabbard set all over with jewels.

" Behind these rode a young squire and a woman. The young squire was so big and well formed, and he had a face that was so handsome and looked so brave and strong, and yet so kind and sunny, too, that I am sure all the girls in the streets of Camelot must have stared at him and at nothing else, as he passed along. And I am just as sure that the men were staring at the woman who rode beside him. For she was young—or she looked young, and that is the same thing for a woman—and she was beautiful, too. They could not see much of her face, because she kept it turned toward the young squire, but they could see the curve of her neck and her dark masses of hair, that fell almost down to the horse's back, all twisted full of pearls. She wore a wonderful, long silk gown, that seemed always changing its color from white to pale blue and back to white again. Sometimes it shone almost like the steel and the silver of the armors, but still it fluttered in the little breezes and looked as soft as any other silk. I suppose, after all, the women noticed this more than the men did.

"The young squire and the woman rode close together, and they seemed to be talking. But the woman could not talk much, because there were so many tears in her voice, though there were few in her eyes. 'What makes you so sorry, Fairy Mother?' the young man said. 'Am I not to be a knight and go on adventures and do brave things, as you have told me, and does not that make you glad and proud?'

"'Oh, yes,' the woman answered, 'I am glad and proud of all that, but I am sorry that I must lose you. Perhaps I shall not see you any more, and surely I shall not see you every day, as I have all these years.'

"The young man himself looked sorry at that. 'I wish I could stay with you, Fairy Mother,' he said; 'but it would not be right, would it, for a strong man like me to stay at home always and never do anything good or great or brave, like other men?'

"'No, no, dear Lancelot, no,' she said; 'it would not be right. I know that you must come to the King now, and stay with him, or go where he sends you, and belong to him and to all the world, and not to me any more.'

"Though the squire was talking with the woman by his side, yet all the while he was looking at the streets and the houses and the people, as if he had never seen such things before. And just now the little procession turned a corner, and he came where he could see the castle of the King, its big, strong, graceful towers, its high walls and battlements, and the ladies standing there and looking down at him and the others. And when he saw the whole castle suddenly before him, looking so grand and stately, his first thought was: 'Can it be that the great King, who owns all this, will let me stay here with him and be his knight? If he only will, it will make me happy all my life to say "I am King Arthur's knight." And that Round Table! Can I hope ever to sit there, too, among the best of all his knights?' Then his eyes grew brighter and his whole face glowed with the joy of this great hope.

"It was just then that he saw the ladies on the wall, and he looked at one who stood among them, and after that he scarcely saw the rest. The evening sun was behind her and her face was darkened, but he could see it a little, and he thought: 'I did not know before that any one could be more beautiful than my Fairy Mother.' And as he saw the soft, low, level light of the sun shining through the gold of her hair, he thought again: 'She wears the halo of a saint.' He could not look away from her, but he touched the hand of the woman beside him and whispered: 'Who is she?'

"And she answered: 'She is the King's wife, Queen Guinevere.' Then suddenly all the light went out of the young man's face, and he looked down at his horse's neck, and he did not speak again till they came to the castle gate.

"The news of the coming of the strangers had run through the castle, and the King himself came down to the gate to meet them. The young squire and the woman dismounted from the horses and knelt before him. 'My lord,' she said, 'I have come to ask a gift of you. It is one that will not cause you any loss.'

"You know in those days kings and lords and knights had a way of promising gifts to people before they knew what was to be asked, and they were as honorable about keeping these promises as they were stupid about making them. But Arthur had a way of promising that he would give what was asked, if it were in reason and if it were not against his honor or his kingdom. And some such answer as this he made to this woman.

"'My lord,' she said, 'here is a young squire, brave and of high birth; here are his sword, his armor, and his horse; I ask you to make him a knight whenever he shall ask it of you.'

"Then Arthur smiled and said: 'You told me that your gift should be no loss to me. When I make a young man a knight I like to give him myself his horse, his armor, and his sword. Is it not a loss to me if you give them to him instead?'

"'Yet, let me do it,' the woman answered. 'Since he was a little child all that he has had has been from me, and these things are the last that I can give him.'

"'It shall be as you wish,' said the King.

"'Then,' said the woman, 'I must go.' She stooped and kissed the forehead of the squire, who still knelt before the King; then she turned away, sprang upon her horse, with no one to help her, hid her face in her veil, and rode away from the gate. For a moment the King scarcely knew what she was doing. 'Do not go yet,' he said; 'the feast of St. John is coming; stay and keep it with us and see your good young squire made a knight.'

"But she was gone already. The young man still kneeling, the horse with the armor on its back, the two squires who led it, and the others who carried the helmet and the sword stayed inside the gate. All the rest followed the strange woman down the long street and out from the gate of Camelot and away, nobody knew where.

"The King took the young man's hand,

raised him up, and led him to the great hall of
the castle. There the Queen came to meet
them and stood beside the King. 'And now,'
the King said, 'tell us who you are.'

" ' My lord,' the young man answered, 'my
Fairy Mother has told me that I am King Ban's
son.'

" ' King Ban's son ! ' cried the King ; 'then
you are a thousand times welcome here ! You
are that Galahad who was promised to me as
the best of all my knights.'

" ' No, my lord,' said the squire, ' I do not
hope to be that, and I am not Galahad.'

" ' But,' said the King again, ' are not you that
son of King Ban whom some woman stole from
his wife and carried down into the lake and
kept? His name was Galahad, and Merlin said
that Galahad should be my best knight.'

" ' I can say nothing of that, my lord,' said
the squire. 'If Merlin told you the truth, let
him make his own words good. It would
make me very proud if I could be counted the
greatest of your knights. If I am never that,
then I shall be glad that you have better
knights than I. But for my name—I never
knew my real father or mother, and I do not
know what name they called me by. I know
only my Fairy Mother, and I will keep the
name she gave me—Lancelot of the Lake.'

" ' Was that your Fairy Mother, as you call

her,' said the King, 'who came with you just
now? You are disobedient, both of you. She
would not let me give you arms and you will
not let me give you a name. But you may
keep whatever name you like. And now tell
me about this Fairy Mother. Who is she?
Was it she who stole you from your real
mother? And what has she done with you all
the years since then?'

"'I will tell you all that I can,' the young man
answered, 'but I do not like to hear you talk
about her stealing me. She is the only mother
I have ever known. Her name is Nimue, and
they call her the Lady of the Lake. I cannot
tell you just what that means. I have never
seen the lake but once in all the years that I
have been with her. I have heard it said sometimes that there was no lake really, but only
an enchantment, an image of a lake, to keep
strangers away from the place where she lived.

"'I do not know how I came to her first, but
as long ago as I can remember she took care
of me and taught me. I was her page, and I
learned to serve her and her maidens as a good
page ought to serve ladies, and I learned to sing
and to play the harp a little. The place where
we lived was not like this. It was a beautiful
place, but not so beautiful as this. There were
fine castles and gardens and a river, but they
did not look like these. We could not see far

away to where the sky comes down and touches the hills, as we can here. From our tower we could look out over the woods, but not very far away it all seemed to stop, and we could see no more. The sun shone warmer than here, yet it did not shine so bright. The air was not clear, like the air here. It was light, but it was all misty, and the sun shone dim.

" ' We had many knights and ladies with us, and other knights and ladies came often to visit us. We had great feasts in the hall of our castle and we had hunts and tournaments. As soon as I could hold a bow and arrow they began to teach me to shoot with them. As soon as I could sit upon a horse I began to learn to ride, and when I was old enough I rode hunting with the knights and the young squires. Then my Fairy Mother gave me a master, who taught me to hold a spear and how to run with it against a quintain, and then against another man on another horse. Day after day and month after month he taught me, till I could use my spear better than he could use his. He taught me to fight with the sword, too, and still I practised with both till none of the knights who lived about us and none of the knights who came to visit us could stand against me in a fight with either. And when in some trial I had beaten all the rest, my Fairy

Mother would take off my helmet and kiss me and say that I should be the best knight of the world some day. I only tell you what she said; you know, my lord, she loved me so much.

"'Once, not very long ago, when some of us were hunting, I rode far away from the rest, and farther away from where we lived than I had ever been before. And suddenly it seemed to me that I was in a more beautiful place than I had ever seen. There was sunlight all around me, brighter than I had ever known, sunlight like this around us here. The sun itself was so bright that I could not look at it—not dusky, as it was where we lived. I could look far away and see the blue sky everywhere, as you can here. It was all so lovely that I stayed for a long time to look, and then, when I thought that it was time for me to go back to my friends, I could not find the way. I turned the way that it seemed to me I ought to go, and there was nothing there but a broad lake, with that strange, clear sunlight shining on it. Then, as I came near the lake, I saw my Fairy Mother coming from its bank. "Give me your hand," she said, and she sprang on my horse's back behind me. She put her arms around me, just as she used to do when I first learned to sit upon a horse, and took the reins out of my hands, and we rode toward the lake.

And then, all at once, I cannot tell you how, the lake was gone, and soon we were in places that I knew, and all the beautiful sunlight was gone, and then we were at home.

"'That night, I do not know whether I was awake or dreaming, but I thought that my Fairy Mother came and stood beside me. She wept and said: "My little Lancelot—my great Lancelot—you have grown too big to stay here with me any more. I cannot keep you here and love you all alone any longer. You must go out into the world, where the King and the Queen and every one will love you, where you can live and fight with other knights and be the best of them all." I only tell you what she said, my lord.

"'And I do not know whether she had told me of you before, my lord, or whether I had heard of you from the knights and ladies who came to visit us, but somehow I knew that your court was the finest and that your knights were the bravest and the greatest in the world. And so, when she told me that I must come to Arthur's court, I knew that I was to serve the noblest of kings. So here I have come, my lord, to ask that I may be your knight.'

"Now, all the time that the young squire had been telling this story he had been looking first at the King and then at the Queen, as

they stood together before him, listening to
every word that he said. He could see the
Queen's face clearly now, of course, and as she
stood there so near him, listening and looking
into his face with her beautiful, kind eyes, he
almost forgot what he was telling, and he
thought: 'I shall never see any other woman
like her, and, since she is the King's and can
never be mine, will it be well for me to stay
here? Shall I not be happier if I go away and
try to forget her?' But when he looked at the
King again and met his eyes, which were just
as kind, and saw how strong and noble and
gentle he looked, he thought again: 'I will
not be such a coward as to run away. I will
stay and be her knight and the King's, and in
all my battles I will remember her and think
that I am fighting for her.'

"'It is a strange story that you have told
us,' said the King. 'Indeed your Fairy
Mother kept you and taught you well, and it
is right that you should hold to the name she
gave you, if you will. We will call you Lancelot, then, and still, for your father's sake, you
shall sit at my Round Table as soon as you
are a knight.'

"And Lancelot only bowed and kissed the
King's hand, but to himself he said: 'Yes, I
will stay and live and fight for both of them.
It will be glory and happiness enough to be

the greatest or the least of the knights of such a king.'

"I sometimes think that it would have been better if Lancelot had left Camelot then and left England and had never come back. Sometimes the bravest men would prove themselves braver if they would only dare to be afraid. And yet, I cannot think what the court of King Arthur would have been without Lancelot. Of one thing I am sure : there would not have been so many good stories.

"'And when,' said the King, 'shall I make you a knight?'

"'May it be to-morrow, my lord?' said Lancelot.

"'Yes,' said the King, 'if you wish it; come here again at noon.'

"Then Lancelot went to the Church of St. Stephen, and there, all night, before the altar, he watched his armor. There were others there, who were to be made knights to-morrow, doing the same. Lancelot scarcely saw them. He scarcely saw his armor there before him. What he did see, all through that night, was the lovely face of the Queen, with the sweet, kind eyes bent on him, as he had seen them when he told his story. The candles on the altar seemed shining through her hair, as the sun had shone through it when she stood on the castle wall. And when the early summer sun lighted the windows of the church and the candles began to look dim, he saw her still. He was thinking of her when he left the church and went to make ready to meet the King.

" He was thinking of her when he came into the great hall of the castle, and he scarcely more than noticed all the people who were there. The hall was filled with ladies and knights, and squires who were to be knights to-day. The King came and stood at the far end of the hall. He was ready for those to whom he was to give knighthood. And then, all at once, Lancelot noticed a terrible thing. He had no sword. He had not thought of it before, and he had left it in the church. Now indeed he saw the people about him. They were all looking at him, he thought, and he saw all their faces dance and swim and whirl around him and all their eyes fixed upon him. He was ready to turn and run from the place, for he thought: 'How they will all laugh at me when they see that I have no sword! And the King will say that I am not worthy to be a knight.'

" And just at that moment he heard a voice behind him, and the voice said: 'Young man, do not turn to look at me or some one may see us. I have brought you your sword. It is here in the fold of my gown. Take it as I pass you, but do not turn your head.'

"The swarming faces around him were gone, and he scarcely understood what the voice behind him had said, because the voice itself was so sweet. And his heart gave a great leap, as he thought: 'That voice is as lovely as the face of the Queen. Are there more of them, then? Is this court of Arthur full of such women as she?' But as the woman who had spoken passed him he took the sword from her hand, and he did not turn his head, but when she had passed and was in front of him he looked at her. She was the Queen.

"He could not think any more now. It was time, and he passed forward through the hall, knelt down and laid his sword at the feet of the King. Dimly he heard the King speaking to him the oath for a new knight—that he should be faithful, gentle, and merciful—that he should fight for the poor—that he should fear shame more than death. But he knew what the oath was and they all heard him when he said: 'I swear it.'

"Then two old knights fastened his spurs, and the Queen herself came and belted on his sword. As she did it the new knight gazed into her face again, and, a moment later, when the King gave him the oath of the Round Table and he swore to be true and loyal in all things to God and to the King, he added, in

his own mind : ' and to the Queen.' But he
did not see her then. His eyes looked straight
into the King's. And it seemed to Arthur
that he saw in those eyes something great and
wonderful, that he had never seen before in
any knight who had sworn this oath. He
could not tell what it was, but it was something
that made him say : 'Oh, Galahad or Lancelot, I know that you will be my best knight.
Come and take the place that has been made
for you.'

"And he led him straight to the Siege Perilous and said : 'Sit here ; it is your place.'
Yet, when the new knight would have taken
the seat, the King himself held him back, for
he looked and there were no letters in it. The
King looked and wondered and paused. It
seemed to him that the magic of the seats must
be sleeping and that soon the letters must ap-
pear. But no letters came, and the King
turned and led the way to the next seat, at the
right of the Siege Perilous. It was blank too,
and the King looked in the next, and so was
that. But when he came to the fourth seat, he
and the knight saw in it the name, in new letters of bright gold—not ' Galahad,' but ' Lancelot of the Lake.'

"And Lancelot took the seat, and in that
seat he sat for many years, whenever he was in
Arthur's court. And the fame of Lancelot

grew all through those many years, with the
fame of Arthur's court. For all over the world
it was said that there was no other court like
Arthur's, and that there was no other knight
like Lancelot. He was the bravest knight in
battle, they said, and in the tournament the
strongest, and everywhere he was the truest,
the noblest, and the gentlest. All good knights
wished that they might be like him, and the
King and the Queen loved him more than any
other.

"And often in those years Arthur would
gaze and gaze at him, and then at the Siege
Perilous, and would think : 'Why does he not
take his place? Why can I not read his name
in that seat? What better knight than he can
I ever have? Who can ever sit there if he
cannot?'

"But no gold letters came in the Siege
Perilous. And after a time there came to the
court a strong young man, Bors, Lancelot's
cousin, the son of King Bors. And when Arthur made him a knight and led him to the
Round Table, his name was found in the seat
next to Lancelot's and nearer to the Siege
Perilous, nearer to the throne. Then Arthur
wondered more, for though Bors was strong
and brave and noble, he never seemed so
good a knight as Lancelot, in the battle or the
tournament. So knights came and went and

knights were killed in battle and new knights
came. And seats were left empty at the Round
Table and other names came in them and
other knights sat in them. Yet no name came
in the Siege Perilous."

CHAPTER V

THE KITCHEN BOY

WE still had an hour or more to wait, before the train would come that was to take us away from Caerleon. It was luncheon-time, too, and so, if we could find the luncheon, we did not mind the waiting. There was a little house near the railway station, and a lantern with a picture of an angel hung over the door. We thought that we might find something to eat in it. A woman stood behind the bar and two men stood in front of it, drinking and talking with the woman. Of all the people who had wondered at our coming to Caerleon not one had yet been so astonished as that woman was when we asked her if we could have luncheon. She could not speak for a minute, and then she said that she was afraid she could not give us anything, and that this was not an hotel.

If we had been English people we should

probably have said something meant to be very
cutting about the word " Hotel " being on the
lantern over the door, in very plain letters.
But, being only common Americans, we took
it very mildly and asked her if she could not
possibly find anything at all ; some bread and
cheese and tea would do. Oh, yes, we could
have those, she said, and she led us into a little
room behind the bar, where there were some
chairs and a table. The two men drank up
their beer as fast as they could and hurried
away to call the rest of the people of the town
together by telling them that three strangers
had come to the Angel and asked for luncheon.
Probably the rest of the people refused to believe it, for none of them came to look at us.
I may as well say now, because I may forget
it by and by, that the luncheon cost us four-
pence each.

" There was a time," I said, as we sat in the
little room behind the bar, " when strangers
who came to Caerleon and asked for something
to eat and drink were treated better than this.
There was the kitchen boy, for instance."

Of course Helen must have known, when
she heard that, that there was some sort of
story about the kitchen boy, and she ought to
have asked what it was. But I suppose she
thought that I would tell it any way and there
was no need of her asking me to. So she went

on drinking her tea, into which her mother had put a great deal of hot water, because that is the right way to make tea for little girls, and all she said was that she would take a little more butter, please. Now of course this was wrong. Children should be heard as well as seen, when they really have anything to say. I knew she was dying to hear that story, still she ought to have said so. I had half a mind not to tell it at all, but then, nobody ever began to tell a story and then stopped just because the other people kept still and listened.

So I waited a little, to show how hurt I felt, and then I said: " You see, King Arthur and his knights had a good deal of fighting to do at first. They had to beat the rebels all around them; they had to drive away the Saxons, who were trying to win the land and destroy the people ; and once, the old books say, the Emperor of Rome sent ambassadors to Arthur to demand of him the tribute that the Emperor said was due from England to Rome. Arthur gave the ambassadors a fine banquet and costly presents for themselves, but no tribute for the Emperor. Then he and his army crossed the channel and beat the Emperor in a great battle and went on to Rome, and there Arthur himself was crowned Emperor. You may believe this story or not, as you like. I don't more than half believe it myself. But in all Arthur's battles, and in all adventures, when there were no battles, Lancelot was counted the best of his knights. And of the others there was none who grew more famous than Gawain. You will hear much of him some time, and so I should like to make you understand what sort of a man he was.

" He was a king's son, and he lived first at his father's court and then at Arthur's. And so he learned all that could be learned to make a good knight. He was brave and he was strong and skilful with his spear and his sword. It was said that he was the most courteous knight of Arthur's court, though I do not believe that any one could be more courteous than Lancelot. Some of the old books say, too, that he could speak so well that nobody could ever refuse him anything that he asked. He knew all that belonged to true knighthood and he loved justice and right and truth and courtesy, when they were on his side, or when he had no side. For I believe that his own real nature was not great and generous, like Lancelot's. No one knew what was brave and right better than he, but he was selfish and hasty and he often forgot what was right, or else saw the right and chose the wrong, because it suited his purpose better. And so he often did things that made him sorry afterward. Still, he did so much that was good, too, that he was always counted one of the best of Arthur's knights.

" Well, if King Arthur and his army really went to Rome, they soon came back, and if they did not go, of course they did not have to come back. And wherever they went and whenever they came, King Arthur almost always managed to keep the great feast of Pentecost here at Caerleon. You have found out, long before this, what queer notions some of the people had in those days. Even King Arthur had a few of them, and one of his was that he would never go to dinner on Pentecost till he had seen some wonderful thing. And wonderful things were so common then that, as far as I have ever heard or read, he did not lose a Pentecost dinner in his whole reign, and only once was he even late for dinner.

" So, one Pentecost, King Arthur and Queen Guinevere and the knights of the court sat in the great hall of the castle and waited for something to happen, so that they could go to dinner. They would all have been delighted if somebody had run in and had told them that there was a snake a mile long coiled three times around some castle somewhere, and that the lady in the castle wanted a knight to come and kill the snake, so that she could get out. Every one of them would have wanted to go, and nothing but their politeness would have

kept them from saying so all at once. But
they did not like to have any delay about dinner.

"And just a few minutes before dinner-time
three men came into the hall and stood before
the King. One of them was taller than the
others, but young—no more than a boy, as it
seemed. He stood between the other two and
leaned on their shoulders, as if he could not
walk alone. Then, when they were before the
King, he pushed them from him, and said: 'My
lord, I have come to ask three gifts of you—
easy gifts for you to grant. One of them I will
ask now and the other two I will ask a year
from this day.'

"When Arthur looked in the boy's face he
saw that flush of frank, free courage, and that
fine, glad light in the eyes that he loved so
much in his younger knights. 'Surely,' he
thought, 'I have none of a better look than he,
unless Lancelot or Gawain.' And he said:
'Ask what you will.'

"'It is only,' said the boy, 'that you will
give me all I need to eat and drink for a year.
At the end of the year I will ask my other
gifts.'

"If the boy had asked for a castle or a city
or two, King Arthur might not have been surprised, but now he was surprised. 'Can I not
give you more than that?' he said 'I would

give that to any beggar, but you look like one who will be a great and brave man some day. Ask something more of me. What is your name?'

"'I will not tell you my name now,' said the boy, 'and I will ask nothing more.'

"'Let it be as you please,' said the King, 'but your gift is one for Sir Kay to give you, not for me.' Then he called Sir Kay, his seneschal, and said: 'Take the boy and give him everything he needs, as if he were a lord's son.'

"'There will be no need of that,' Kay answered; 'he is no doubt some common fellow. If he were a lord's son he would ask for a horse or armor or something else worth having. But he shall have enough to eat and he shall work with the other boys in the kitchen. He wants to get his food and drink for nothing, I suppose. Look at his big, white hands. If he will not tell us his name I will give him one. We will call him Fairhands.'

"Now King Arthur thought that all this was quite as wonderful as anything he was likely to see, so he felt that he had a right to go to dinner. The two men who had come with the boy went away, and Fairhands, as Kay called him, was sent down to the far end of the hall, among the other boys. There he ate his dinner, and when it was over, Kay sent him to the kitchen and he was set to work.

"And every day for a whole year he was there in the kitchen. He built fires and brought water and scoured pots and pans. He ate what the other boys ate, and never complained that he had too much work or too little play. He did have some play, for the boys had games of strength and skill among themselves, and he was the best at all of them. And always, when he was not at work, he liked to be where he could see the knights. He always tried to see the tournaments. He almost held his breath when the knights clashed together, and he threw up his cap and cheered when Lancelot and Gawain did best among the knights, as they always did.

"For Lancelot and Gawain were his friends. They had seen him when he came into the hall and asked the King for food and drink. They did not believe, like the sharp-tongued Kay, that he was some common fellow. They saw his fine, clear eyes, and the courage in his face and the strong, graceful, easy way in which he bore himself. They wondered why he would not tell his name, but they believed that some time he would make it known all through the world. So they would call him often from among the other boys and take him to their own rooms in the castle. They asked him his name many times, but he would never tell them. They offered him better things to eat

"For a whole year he was there in the kitchen."

than the boys in the kitchen had, but he would take nothing. He would have nothing, he said, but what Kay gave him, till the time came for him to ask his other gifts of the King.

"And when Pentecost came again the court was here at Caerleon, and the King and the Queen and the knights sat in the great hall of the castle, waiting again for something wonderful to happen, so that they could have dinner. Then, as they waited, they heard a horse's hoofs in the court-yard, and in a moment a girl ran into the hall and went straight toward the King. She knelt before him and cried: 'My lord, a wicked knight is keeping my sister prisoner, and she has sent me to ask that you will send some one of your knights to fight with him and free her.'

"'Where is your sister?' the King asked. 'How does the knight keep her a prisoner? What is her name and what is yours?'

"'I must not tell you her name or mine,' the girl answered, 'but she lives in the Castle Perilous, and she is a great lady. The knight is called the Red Knight of the Red Plains. He stays before the gate of the castle and fights with all the knights that come to free her, and kills them, and he will not let anybody come into the castle or go out of it, unless he chooses. But we heard that the best knights of the world were in your court, and my sister told me to

say that if one of them would come and kill
the wicked knight she would marry him and
he should have her castle and all her lands.'

"Of all the strange notions of those days I
think that pretty nearly the strangest were
those that some people had about keeping their
names secret. There was no reason in the
world, that I can see, why this girl should not
tell her name, yet I suppose she would rather
let her sister stay shut up in her castle for the
rest of her life than tell it, when she had made
up her mind not to.

"'I have knights here, no doubt,' said the
King, 'who could beat the Red Knight of the
Red Plains and free your sister, but I cannot
send any of them unless you tell me your name
and hers.'

"'Then I must look for a knight somewhere
else,' said the girl, and she turned to go out of
the hall.

"Then, from among those who stood far
down the hall, away from the King and the
girl, came a voice that cried: 'My lord, my
lord, a year ago you promised me two gifts;
the time has come for me to ask them.'

"The King looked to see whose voice it was,
and saw the kitchen boy. He remembered
what had passed a year ago, and said: 'Yes,
the time has come; ask your gifts.'

"The kitchen boy knelt before the King and

said : 'My lord, send me with this damsel to free her sister. This is the first gift I ask.'

"'You always ask things that are hard for me to give,' the King answered. 'This is not an adventure for you to try. Did you not hear her say that this Red Knight of the Red Plains had killed other knights who had come to free her sister? You are little more than a boy yet. Leave such hard fighting for harder and older men. Stay here at my court; leave the kitchen; practise with the young squires; learn how to sit upon your horse and how to use your spear and your shield and your sword. Then you can fight as well as the bravest. Do not try too much now and make me lose such a good knight as you might grow to be.'

"'Perhaps, my lord,' said the kitchen boy, 'I know more of these things already than you think, and it is this that I ask. It is not against your honor to give it to me, and you cannot deny me my two gifts. Let me go to free this lady.'

"Then, as the King gazed into the boy's eyes, that were looking straight into his, it seemed to him that he lost sight of the poor kitchen garments and saw only the bright young face and the frank, free courage, as he had seen it before, and again he thought: 'I have none of a better look than he, unless

Lancelot or Gawain.' And still the eyes
begged of him: 'Let me go,' and the King
nodded and answered them : 'Go, if you will.'

"'And my other gift, my last one,' said the
boy; 'it is this: I have long wished that Sir
Lancelot might make me a knight—Sir Lancelot, and no one else. Let him follow me, as I
go away with the damsel, and let him make
me a knight whenever I ask him.'

"'That gift I will give you,' said the King,
'most gladly of all,' and he turned and nodded
toward Lancelot. And Lancelot looked more
proud to hear the boy ask this than he would
have looked if he had fought and beaten the
greatest knight of all the world except himself. I do not believe that anything can be
more delightful to a simple, honest, brave man,
than the admiration of a simple, honest, brave
boy.

"But the girl came back and stood before
the King—she did not kneel this time—and she
said: 'We heard that at your court, King
Arthur, we could find the truest kindness and
justice and courtesy in all the world; but it is
not so. You insult women who come to you
for help. I asked you for a knight to free my
sister, and you give me a kitchen boy, one who
knows how to turn a spit or clean a pot, but
not how to ride a horse or use a spear.' She
turned and walked away again, down the hall,

and Arthur made no answer, but let her go
out and take her horse and ride off along the
road and out of sight.

"The kitchen boy had left the hall too, and
at the gate of the castle he found a big, strong
horse, that was led by a dwarf. And on the
horse's back was a beautiful suit of armor, and
the dwarf carried a sword. The kitchen boy
knew the dwarf and he knew that the horse
and the armor had been sent for him. There
was no shield and no spear. I can't think why
anybody should send a present of a horse and
armor without any spear or shield, but I have
to tell you the story just as it happened. The
dwarf helped the boy to put on the armor and
then he mounted his horse and rode away
after the girl.

"Now the King thought that all that he had
just seen was so wonderful that he was never
likely to have a better right to eat dinner in his
life. So he sat down at the table with the
Queen and all the knights, except two, and the
dinner began. One of the two who did not
sit down was Lancelot. He went to put on
his armor, so that he could follow the kitchen
boy. The other was Sir Kay. Kay was always doing some silly thing or other. It was
he, you know, who had laughed at the boy, and
named him Fairhands, and had set him to work
in the kitchen. He had always hated him, and

now he too resolved to ride after him and punish him. He put on his armor, found a fast horse, and rode quickly along the way that the girl and Fairhands had taken. And just as the kitchen boy came up with the girl he heard Kay's voice behind him. ' Kitchen boy,' he cried, ' come back ! Do you not know me ? Why have you run away from me ? Do you not know that I am your master ? '

" ' I know you,' the boy answered; ' you are Sir Kay, but you are not my master any more. Will you fight with me and prove whether you are or not ? '

" Now this would have been a good chance for the girl to run away from Fairhands, if she really wanted to, but she thought that she was going to see him nicely punished for the impudence of following her, so she stayed to see the fight. You see what Kay was doing was worse than silly. He had his long spear and his shield and Fairhands had neither. It was unknightly to fight with a man who was so much worse armed than himself, unless he had done some great wrong. Kay knew this just as well as anybody, and so I am glad that the fight came out just as it did.

" For when Kay spurred his horse and charged against Fairhands, the boy was not a bit afraid, but galloped straight at him, with his sword drawn and no other weapon. With this he struck the point of Kay's spear away from him and then wounded him in the side, so that he fell down off his horse and lay on his back in the road. Now when one knight beat another in a fair fight he had a right to take his horse and all his arms, if he wanted them. So the kitchen boy took Kay's shield and spear, which he needed, and mounted his horse again to ride on with the girl. Kay got up and went back toward the castle, and the girl, who was a good deal disappointed not to have seen Fairhands soundly beaten, rode on very sulkily.

"But Lancelot had been riding after them, and had seen the whole of the fight with Kay, and now he came up with them. 'My lord, Sir Lancelot,' cried the boy, 'will you try a joust with me?' Lancelot said nothing, but closed his helmet and put his spear in rest, and the girl stopped again to look.

"But this time the boy charged against another sort of knight. For Lancelot's spear struck the middle of his shield and bore him back over the tail of his horse, and he fell in the dust of the road. But his own spear had struck well too, and even the great Lancelot had almost fallen from his saddle. The boy sprang to his feet and cried: 'Will you fight with me now on foot?'

"In an instant Lancelot was off his horse and

had his sword drawn, and then they fought for
a long time, and each of them fought his best.
And Lancelot was thinking all the while:
'Who can this boy be, and where did he learn
to fight so well? It is all that I can do to
guard myself against him. I know the ways of
all the best knights, and Gawain might fight
like this, but who else?' And then he said
aloud: 'Is not this enough, young man? We
have no quarrel, and you have proved yourself
a strong fighter.'

"'Have I proved myself so?' said the
kitchen boy, and his voice trembled with
happiness and pride. 'It did me good to fight
with you, to feel how strong you were, and to
feel that I was strong too, to stand against
you. And do you think that I shall some time
be a good knight?'

"'I know you will,' Lancelot answered, 'if
you live, and now I am not afraid, as I was, to
see you go to fight this Red Knight of the Red
Plains.'

"'Then, my lord, Sir Lancelot,' said the
young man, 'will you give me the order of
knighthood?'

"'Gladly,' said Lancelot; 'but you must tell
me your name first. I will tell it to no one
else if you wish it to be a secret.'

"'It is not a secret from you, Sir Lancelot,'
said the boy, 'but do not tell any others yet—

not till I have done something to make them remember my name. I am Gareth of Orkney. King Lot is my father and I am Gawain's brother. And there at King Arthur's court even he did not know me, I was so small when he left us. It was my mother, Queen Bellicent, who sent me this horse and this armor.'

" Then Lancelot looked in his face again and understood it all, his strength, his courage, his beauty, his noble bearing; but he said: ' Why did you let them keep you in the kitchen all that year, and never tell the King or Gawain or me who you were?'

"'I scarcely know,' said Gareth, 'why I did it. But when I came I asked only for food and drink at first, because I wanted to see what the court was like. I wanted to see the King and you and my brother Gawain. I feared that I was not old enough to be a knight, yet I wanted to be near the King and near you, my lord. And then, when they put me in the kitchen and made me work there, I would not say that I was afraid to do it, so I stayed there and waited for my time. Was it not right for me to do so, and will you not make me a knight now?'

"'Kneel down, then,' said Lancelot, and he touched Gareth's shoulder with his sword and said: 'Rise, Sir Gareth, and may God make you a good knight.'

" And Sir Gareth rose and spoke not another

word, but mounted his horse and was ready to follow the girl. And Lancelot mounted too and rode back. Then the girl said: 'Kitchen boy, go away from me, and do not dare to follow me. I cannot bear to have you near me, for your clothes are greasy and you smell of the kitchen. And do not think that I will let you come with me because you threw that poor knight off his horse and wounded him. That was only an unlucky chance, and often the worst of men can kill the best in that way. And as for your seeming to fight so well with this Lancelot, he let you do it, I have no doubt, just for a spite to me. For he is one of those lazy knights that sit about this Arthur and help him insult ladies who come to him for aid. We beg him to send us knights, and he sends us kitchen boys, and then these brave men stay there in their big castle all together, and eat and drink and laugh at us, and tell one another how mighty they are, and then go to sleep. Keep away from me. I would not have a knight from that court now, and surely not a kitchen boy.'

"'Say what you will to me,' Gareth answered; 'I will try not to come too near to you, but my horse is as fast as yours, and I shall follow you. My King has sent me to free your sister, and I shall free her or I shall die in trying to do it.'

"'You had better go back while you can,' the girl said again. 'If you go on with me you will meet two knights not far from here and you will have to fight with them. They are real knights, and they will make you wish that you were back washing dishes. Perhaps you know how to kill pigs with that sharp-pointed pole of yours, but you do not know how to kill knights or how to keep them from killing you with that platter of a shield.' Then she rode away quickly and Gareth rode after her and answered not a word.

"Soon the road led through a forest, and then they came to a river, with a shallow place where they must cross. And on the other side of the river were two knights, armed and on horseback, and one of them called out: 'Knight, you cannot cross here unless you fight with us.'

"'Will you go back now,' said the girl, 'or will you let them butcher you, like a stupid ox?'

"'I would not turn back if there were six of them,' said Gareth, and he spurred his horse and rode into the river. And just in the middle of the river one of the knights met him. Each, with his spear, struck the middle of the other's shield, and both the spears were broken. Then they drew their swords and struck at each other, till Gareth gave the knight a blow on the helmet that stunned him, and he fell off his horse into the river, and the swift-flowing water rolled him over and over, and the weight of his armor made him sink into a deeper place, and he was drowned.

"Then Gareth rode on through the river and met the other knight on the farther bank. He had no spear now, but the other knight's spear was broken against his shield, and again they both drew their swords and fought, till a stroke of Gareth's sword cut through the other knight's helmet and he fell and lay upon the ground. And Gareth took another spear, that had belonged to the knight, because he had broken his own, and rode on after the girl.

"'Keep away from me,' she cried again; 'you smell of the kitchen and I cannot bear it. Coward! Coward! One of those two poor knights was drowned because his horse slipped in the river; then you came behind the other and struck him like a traitor. Do not come near me.'

"I hope you see, without my telling you, how foolish and false and cruel this girl was. Some silly people think that only men need to be brave, and therefore that only men can be insulted by being called cowards. It is not true. It is a woman's duty to be strong and brave, just as much as a man's. Many women are brave, of course—most women, perhaps— but some are not, and of all those who are not, those who are like this girl are among the very worst. Do you see why ? If any man had said to this kitchen boy what she said, he would have had to fight him, but she knew that he was too good and brave a man to harm a woman. So she dared to call him a coward just because she knew he was not one. I can scarcely think of anything that is more wicked and cruel and heartless for a woman to do than to wrong a man because she knows that he is too brave to take revenge. And if anyone ever tells you that Gareth afterward married this girl—but I will tell you about that by and by. She did not deserve ever to see the face of a brave, true man, much less be married to one.

" It was getting a little dark now, partly because it was late in the day by this time and partly because they were riding into a thicker part of the forest. The girl had to let her horse go more carefully and more slowly and Gareth easily kept near her. ' There is time still for you to go back,' she said ; ' I see that all you do is by chance and not because you know how to fight. If you keep on you will be killed.'

" ' I may be killed,' Gareth answered again, ' but I will go with you, and if I am not killed I will win your sister.' I think, after all, that the bravest thing about Gareth was that he was so ready to win a woman and marry her, when all he knew about her was that she was the sister of such a girl as this.

"Then, all at once, they came to an open space in the woods. There was more light to see by, and yet what they saw seemed gloomier and darker than all that they had seen before. For all the ground was black, as if a fire had been over it, and there was a black thorn tree, and on it hung a black banner and a black shield. A black spear leaned against the black tree, and near by stood a big black horse, all covered with trappings of black silk. And near by too sat a knight, and all his armor was black. The girl drew her rein and almost hissed at Gareth: 'It is the Black Knight of the Black Plain; run, run! You have time yet; he is not on his horse!'

"Then the Black Knight saw them and said: 'Damsel, is this a knight of Arthur's court that you have brought to be your champion?'

"'No,' she answered, 'it is Arthur's kitchen boy.'

"'And why does he come on a horse and in armor? You are of high birth, and it is a shame to you to ride with such an one as he.'

"'He will not leave me,' she answered again; 'and indeed I wish that you could rid me of him. Kill him or drive him away; it is nothing to me which you do.'

"'There is no need of killing him,' said the Black Knight. 'I will take his horse and armor and let him go.'

"'You are too ready,' said Gareth, 'to tell us what you will do with my horse and my armor. I mean to pass this place in spite of you, and you will never get my horse or my armor unless you win them of me in a fair fight, so let us see what you can do.'

"Then the Black Knight got on his horse and they rode together with a mighty crash. And the Black Knight's spear shivered against Gareth's shield, and Gareth's spear pierced the Black Knight through the side and then broke off and left a piece of it sticking in the wound. Yet he drew his sword, and so did Gareth, and they fought with the swords till the Black Knight fainted and fell down off his horse. Then Gareth took off the Black Knight's armor, because it was better than his own, and dressed himself in it. He took his shield too, and he got upon his horse again and rode after the girl.

"'Keep farther from me,' she cried; 'I cannot bear the smell of your dirty kitchen clothes. You have killed another poor knight, by some bad luck. But you will meet one soon who will not let you go so easily. You had better go back now, while you can.'

"'You say that always,' Gareth answered; 'every time that I overthrow a knight you tell me that the next one will kill me. I may be a bad fighter, as you say, yet always when you say so, somehow my enemy goes down before me, and I ride on with you. And so I will ride on with you till I am killed or till I free your sister.'

"Almost as he said this a knight came riding toward them as fast as his horse could run. The way through the woods was growing darker yet, but by the light that was left Gareth saw that the armor and the shield of the knight were all green, and his horse had green trappings. The knight stopped when he saw them and shouted : ' Are you my brother, the Black Knight of the Black Plain? Why do you come here with this damsel?'

" ' This is not your brother,' the girl answered ; ' this is a boy from King Arthur's kitchen, who has killed your brother the Black Knight and has taken his armor and his shield.'

" ' Then I will kill him for killing my brother !' the green knight cried. And without any more words they rushed together and both their spears were broken. Then they drew their swords and fought till the green knight's horse slipped and fell. The knight was on his feet in a moment and Gareth sprang off his horse to the ground and they fought again. Then the girl cried: 'Green knight, why do you fight so long with a coward of a boy? Beat him quickly, as a knight like you ought to beat such a boy, and let me go on my way.'

"And it made the knight ashamed to think that it was only a boy who was fighting so hard against him, and he struck a great stroke with his sword at Gareth and split his shield, so that it fell in two pieces to the ground. But Gareth had heard what the girl said, too, and he thought: 'I would rather die ten times than let her see me beaten.' And he struck a great blow, too, and it fell on the helmet of the green knight and brought him down upon his knees. Then Gareth sprang upon him and caught him by the helmet, and pulled him flat upon the ground, and began to cut the lacing of his helmet, so that he could cut off his head. And the green knight cried: 'You have conquered! The fight is yours! Do not kill me!'

"'It is not for me to give you your life,' Gareth answered; 'I am riding with this damsel to save her sister and you stood in our way; she hates me, but I am her knight till I come where her sister is. If she asks me to spare you, I will spare you.'

"'I ask you to spare him?' she said; 'never, never! How should I ask anything of a poor, dirty kitchen boy?'

"'You hear what she says,' said Gareth; 'I must kill you.'

"But the green knight cried again: 'Save me and I will give myself up to you, with all the knights that are under me. There are thirty

of them, and we will always fight for you, and
go where you wish, and do what you will.'

"'I cannot give you your life,' said Gareth
again, 'unless she asks it of me,' and he pulled
off the knight's helmet and raised his sword, as
if he would strike off his head.

"'Do not dare to kill him!' the girl cried;
'how should a wretched boy like you kill a
good knight?'

"'Damsel,' Gareth answered, 'you have
asked his life of me; he shall have it. Rise, sir
knight, and thank the damsel for saving you.'

"But the green knight only rose upon his
knee. 'Sir,' he said, 'I do not know what you
are. I do not know why this damsel who rides
with you calls you what she does. But I know
that you are a better knight than I; you have
spared my life and I am your servant. It is
almost night and you cannot go much farther.
My castle is near here. Come to it with me
and stay till morning.'

"Now this is one thing that I like about
those old fellows. After they were done fighting about nothing they never had any hard
feelings. The one who was beaten acknowl-
edged it and there was nothing that he could
do for the one who had beaten him that he
would not do. And whatever he was told to
do, no matter how unpleasant it was, he did it if
it took him ten years, as if it were the only thing

he had to live for. And there was many a knight of the worse sort who would plunder and rob and murder, but who would never break a promise that he had made to a knight who had beaten him in a fair fight.

"So Gareth and the girl went to the green knight's castle. But when it was time for supper and the knight led them to the table, the girl said: 'I cannot sit and eat with a common, mean servant like him. It is not courteous of you, sir knight, to put him at the table with one of high birth like me.'

"And the knight answered: 'It is not courteous of you, damsel, to speak so of this noble knight. I do not know who he is, but I never fought with a better knight, and I dare say he is as well born as you or I.' Then he led Gareth to a little side-table and told him to sit there. And he came and sat with him himself and the girl was left to sit and eat her supper alone at the long table in the middle of the hall. And when it was time to go to bed the green knight set many good knights to watch around Gareth, to see that no harm was done to him while he slept.

"And in the morning, when they were ready to leave the castle, the knight said to Gareth: 'My lord, I and my thirty knights are all your servants; what shall we do?'

"'Go with your thirty knights,' said Gareth,

'to King Arthur, and tell him that his kitchen boy sent you. Then do whatever he commands you.'

"'I shall go, my lord,' the green knight answered. 'But now tell me, damsel,' he said, turning to the girl, 'where are you leading this young knight?'

"'He is going with me,' she said, 'to the siege of the Castle Perilous, to free my sister from the knight that keeps her shut up there.'

"'I know him,' said the green knight. 'He is the Red Knight of the Red Plains, is he not? He is one of the strongest knights of the world, for they say he has the strength of seven men. And you are Lynette, are you not, and your sister is the Lady Lyonors?'

"'Yes,' she answered, 'I am Lynette and my sister is the Lady Lyonors.'

"And so Gareth and Lynette rode on their way. But the girl rode for a long time without looking at Gareth or saying a word. Then she stopped her horse and waited for him to come up. But he stopped, too, because she had told him so often not to ride too near her, and then she turned and called to him to come. And when he was by her side she did not look at him, but turned her face away and kept her eyes fixed upon the ground on the other side of her horse. And she said: 'We are not far now from my sister's castle. This Red Knight of

the Red Plains, whom you must fight, is one
of the greatest knights of all the world. I do
not know whether anyone could beat him, except Sir Lancelot or Sir Gawain. But I see
now that you are a good knight. I cannot
guess who you are, but I have seen that you
were stronger than any of the knights we have
met. And all the time I have said harsh and
cruel things to you and you have never answered me with any unkind word. And I
know from that that you are as gentle and as
patient as you are strong. I believe now that
you are of some noble blood, and I long to know
who you are, but I will not ask you, if you do
not wish to tell me. I only ask you now to forgive me, if you can, and to come and fight with
this Red Knight of the Red Plains. And
when you meet him, be as brave as I have seen
you before. Forget me then, and forget how
wicked and cruel I was, and think only that you
are fighting for my sister. She is not like me.'

" ' Damsel,' said Gareth, ' I should not be the
good knight that you say I am, if I could not
bear all that you have said to me and more.
What you said did not make me angry with
you, but it made me angry with the enemy
who was before me. For, after all that you had
said, I could bear anything rather than let you
see me beaten. And now that I have made
you think me brave, it seems to me that there

is no knight living whom I could not fight. And now I will tell you my name, too, since you wish it. I am Gareth of Orkney. My father is the King of Orkney, and Gawain is my brother.'

"Perhaps, after you have been a girl for a few years longer than you have already, you may understand something about girls, but I never shall. I shall never understand why this Lynette should be purposely cruel and heartless to this poor, brave Gareth, and then all at once so sweet and honest. Was it because the green knight had treated him so well, or because she was afraid he would not fight for her sister? Or was it for some other reason, or no reason? What do you think? For myself, I believe that if there ever lived an arrant coward of a girl it was this Lynette on the first day that she rode with Gareth. Yet on this second day, if another knight had knocked him off his horse and left him wounded, she would not have screamed and fainted, as many better girls than she would do. She would have gone to him and taken off his armor and dressed his wounds and taken care of him as well as a surgeon and a nurse together could have done. I know she would have done it, because she did do just such things afterward. I don't like her, but there was some good in her, and, once more, I don't understand her.

"They rode side by side now, and in the afternoon they came to a hermit's cell. 'We are near the castle,' said Lynette, and she spoke low, as if she were afraid the Red Knight of the Red Plains would hear her, but they were not near enough for that. 'A holy man lives here, and here my sister sends bread and meat and wine for any knight who may come to fight for her.'

"They left their horses and went into the cell. The hermit brought them food and drink, and said: 'Sir knight, do not go farther to-day. You have ridden long and your horse is weary. Perhaps you are so, too. Rest here to-night, and to-morrow you can fight the better.'

"So they stayed all night with the hermit, and the next day they rode on again. It was not far now that they rode through the woods, and then, with a turn of the road, they saw all at once an open space, with many tents, and across it the walls and towers of the castle. And Lynette whispered: 'The Red Knight of the Red Plains and his men live in those tents. Do you see that horn, made of an elephant's tusk, hanging on the tree? You must blow that to tell him that you have come to fight with him. But do not blow it yet. Every morning he grows stronger and stronger till noon, and then he has the strength of seven men. And after noon he grows weaker again, so wait till noon is past before you blow the horn. He will be strong enough then.'

" ' No,' said Gareth, ' I do not care how strong he is ; I will fight with him now,' and he rode up to where the horn was and blew a great blast on it, so that the walls of the castle sent back the sound, and all the woods rang with it. And in an instant the place was alive with men. The Red Knight of the Red Plains came from his tent and some of the men put on his armor, while others brought his shield and his spear and his horse, and saddled the horse and held him ready. But Gareth scarcely saw him, for Lynette touched his arm and pointed to the castle, and there, at a window, stood the Lady Lyonors. She saw him and waved her hand to him, and he saw the paleness of her face, and yet a little flush of hope in it, he thought, as she looked at him, and it made him feel stronger for the fight.

" But he could not look at her long, for the Red Knight was on his horse, and his spear was down. And Gareth closed his helmet and put his spear in the rest and was ready too. And when they ran together there was such á crash of the spears upon the shields, and of the shields against the armor, that it seemed to those who heard it that they themselves could feel the shock, and the Lady Lyonors turned away her head and did not dare to look. But Lynette looked, and she saw both the knights and both the horses fall and roll upon the ground. In a moment both the men were up and had drawn their swords, and then Lynette and the Lady Lyonors and all the rest looked and held their breath while the sword strokes showered upon the shields and the helmets.

"Gareth had had no such fight as this before. There was something to fight for now— fame and honor and life—and the Lady Lyonors. Yet he remembered what he had heard of this knight's strange strength. Hard as he fought, he fought carefully too, for it was not noon yet. If he could only bear up and defend himself for a little while, he thought, he should afterwards have the better of the fight. So he used his shield and his sword to keep off the blows that the Red Knight rained upon him, and he struck few himself. He tried to save all his strength till his own time should come, and all the while he felt the strokes of the Red Knight's sword fall heavier and faster and sharper, and pieces of his shield were hewn off, and the rivets of his armor were loosened, and links of his mail were cut and hung useless. And when it seemed to him that he could stand no more and that he must sink down under the very weight and fury of that terrible, fierce sword, suddenly he felt the force of it grow less. It fell no longer so quick or so hard on his shield and his helmet as before. It was noon, and the Red Knight was losing that magic strength that had been growing all this time. Soon it would all leave him and the fight would be a fair one. The new hope made Gareth stronger and he rushed upon his enemy and drove him backward across the field, till the Red Knight cried out: 'Sir knight, we have fought too long! Let us both rest a little and then we can fight better.'

"So they both sat down and took off their helmets and breathed the fresh air. And as he rested Gareth looked up at the castle window and saw again the Lady Lyonors looking down at him. And it seemed to him that the look in her face was not as it had been at first. It was almost hopeless before, and yet there was no fear in it. But now he thought that there were hope and fear both. 'What has she to fear?' he thought; 'if I am killed nothing worse will come to her than has come already; can it be that the fear is for me?'

"And with that thought he cried out: 'Come, Red Knight of the Red Plains, let us go on with our fight and have it done! I am ready for you!'

"And they rushed together and fought again till the woods and the castle echoed with the blows of their swords and the clatter of their armor. And the Red Knight was still strong and Gareth was weary with guarding himself as he had done against that mighty power that he had before noon, so that his head began to swim and his eyes grew dim and the Red Knight seemed to rise taller and bigger and to tower over him like a giant. And not the knight alone, but everything around him seemed red like blood, and it all floated and twisted and curled before his eyes, and Gareth reeled and almost fell, and then he heard the voice of Lynette, as if it came out of that strange, whirling, bloody mist, and it cried: 'Oh, Sir Gareth, where are the courage and the strength that I have seen you show? My sister stands there at the window and weeps to see you beaten by this cruel knight.'

"And when he heard those words the red mist was gone from before Gareth's eyes, and he made a last rush upon his foe. He struck one fierce blow upon the Red Knight's sword and drove it out of his hand, and then another upon his helmet and felled him to the ground. Then he sprang upon him and cut the lacings of his helmet and tore it off and stood ready to strike off his head. And the Red Knight cried: 'You have won; you are a better knight than I; give me my life!'

"'Why should I let you live?' Gareth answered. 'You have killed many knights, they say, who came here to help this lady; it is your turn now. Yet, before I kill you, tell me why you came here and shut her up so in her own castle.'

" ' I will tell you,' said the Red Knight; ' once I loved a lady ; she had a brother, and a knight of Arthur's court killed him. It was Lancelot or Gawain, we did not know which. Then the lady whom I loved told me to kill Lancelot or Gawain or both of them to avenge her brother. And I came here and besieged this castle, because I thought that the lady of the castle would send to King Arthur for help, and that Lancelot or Gawain would come and fight with me. But now I am punished enough, because I am beaten in a fight, yet not by Lancelot or Gawain.'

" ' It was all wrong that you did,' said Gareth, ' for if Lancelot or Gawain killed your lady's brother I know that he did it in a fair fight, and any knight may chance to be killed so. Yet I will spare you now, if the lady of this castle forgives you.' And he looked up at the window of the castle again, and the Lady Lyonors made a sign to him to give the Red Knight his life. 'Live, then,' Gareth said, 'and go to the court of King Arthur, with all your men. Find Lancelot and Gawain both, and beg them to forgive you for all the ill-will you have had toward them.

Then do whatever they and the King command you.'

"So the Red Knight of the Red Plains rose from the ground where he lay and stood before Gareth with bowed head, and he said: 'You have made me ashamed of all that I have done. For if I had beaten you in this fight I should not have spared you as you have spared me. I should have killed you. If Lancelot and Gawain and the rest at King Arthur's court are like you it was wrong for me ever to be against them.'

"And the story says that the Red Knight of the Red Plains went to the court, as Gareth told him to do. And there he stayed for a long time and lived and fought well, and after a time he came to be a knight of the Round Table.

"And now there is only a word more. Some time, I hope, you will learn to love the greatest poet of our time as much as I love him. He has told this story better than it ever was told before or will be told again. Yet, when you read the story as he tells it, and he says at the end of it that Gareth married Lynette, remember what I tell you now, he did not marry her. I learned the story from the same book where he learned it, and I tell you that Gareth married the Lady Lyonors."

CHAPTER VI

THE SPARROW-HAWK

"WHAT are we going to Cardiff for?" Helen's mother asked. We were in a train on our way there, and it puzzled her greatly. She had known many people who had travelled much, but she had never heard of anybody going to Cardiff before.

"We are going to Cardiff," I said, "just because Geraint went there."

"Who was Geraint?" said Helen; "and how do you know he went to Cardiff?" said her mother; "and what did he go there for?" said Helen; "and what if he did?" said her mother.

You know how hopeless it is to answer people who ask questions like this, so I only said, with all the dignity that I thought I could make them believe in, "Ladies, with the perfect understanding that you have no right at all to question where we go, since you have left this journey all to me, I will tell you some-thing about Geraint and why he went to Car-diff. As for ourselves, I can only say again that we are going there because Geraint did."

They did not seem a bit frightened at seeing how firm I was, but Helen could not help show-ing that she saw a story coming. "Still," her mother said, "you had better keep right on looking out of the window, because you might miss seeing something, and you can hear just as well."

"I have told you before," I began, "that King Arthur usually kept the feast of Pente-cost at Caerleon. This that I am going to tell you about happened on the Tuesday after Pentecost, just to be exact. The King and the Queen and the knights were dining in the great hall of the castle, when there came in a tall, fair-haired young man. He came and stood before the King and said: 'My lord, I am one of your foresters, in the Forest of Dean. To-day I saw a great stag in the forest. It was pure white, and it was so beautiful and proud that it would not go with any of the other ani-mals, but kept by itself. And I came to ask you if anything should be done.'

"'You have done well,' said the King; 'to-morrow we will all hunt this stag. Let the word be given to all in the castle, and we will start at daybreak.'

" And the Queen said: ' Will you let me go, my lord, to see the hunting of this wonderful stag?'

" ' Gladly,' the King answered, 'if you will be ready with the rest at daybreak.'

" And Gawain said : ' My lord, will it not be well if you command that whoever may kill the stag shall have its head to keep or to give to whom he pleases?'

" ' It shall be so,' the King answered.

" And so at daybreak the King and his knights and attendants and squires and pages were up and ready for the hunt. But the Queen was still asleep. Some of them wanted to wake her, but Arthur said: 'No; if she would rather sleep than see the hunt, let her sleep.'

" But when they were all gone the Queen awoke. Then she called some of her maidens and told them to go to the stable and bring horses, so that they could follow the hunters. But they could find only two horses, so the Queen and one of her maidens took these and rode away toward the Usk. They came to the river, I suppose, not far from where the bridge is, where we stood this morning. But there was no bridge then, and their horses had to wade through the river. Then they followed the track of the hunters through the woods on the other side.

" In a few moments they heard the galloping of a horse, and a young knight rode up to them. He was a tall, handsome fellow. He wore a robe of silk, and around his body was a purple scarf, with a gold apple at each corner, and by his side was a sword with a gold hilt. This was Geraint. His father was Erbin, the King of Devon.

" ' Why did you not go with the others to the hunt, Geraint ? ' the Queen asked.

" ' Because I did not know when they went,' he answered.

" ' It was so with me,' said the Queen, ' for I was asleep, but perhaps we can hear something of the hunt from where we are now ; we can at least hear the horns and the dogs.'

" And, as they stood waiting, there came past them a knight, all in armor, on a big horse, and a lady on another horse, and a dwarf on a third horse. ' Geraint,' said the Queen, ' do you know who that knight is ? '

" Geraint did not know and the Queen sent her maiden to ask the dwarf what was his master's name. ' I will not tell you his name,' the dwarf answered.

" ' Then I will go and ask the knight himself,' said the maiden.

" ' You shall not ask him,' said the dwarf ; you are not of high enough rank to speak to my lord.'

"Then, as the maiden turned her horse to go toward the knight, the dwarf struck her with his whip across the face, and she rode away from him and came back to the Queen.

"'I will go now and ask him myself who his master is,' said Geraint. But the dwarf gave him the same answer that he had given to the maiden.

"'Then,' said Geraint, 'I will go and ask the knight himself.'

"'You shall not ask him,' said the dwarf; 'you are not of high enough rank to speak to my lord.'

"And as Geraint turned away from the dwarf and toward the knight, the dwarf struck him across the face, just as he had struck the maiden. For an instant Geraint had his hand on the hilt of his sword, and he could have killed the dwarf with one stroke of it. Then he thought that it would be unworthy of a man like him to kill such a weak, wretched creature as the dwarf, and he thought, too, that it would be of no use for him to fight with the knight, because the knight was fully armed and he had only his sword. So he rode back to the Queen and said: 'With your leave, I will follow this knight, and when he comes to any place where I can get arms I will try to avenge the insult to you which his dwarf did in striking your maiden.'

"'Go, then, Geraint,' the Queen answered, 'and I shall be grateful for your service to me. Do not try to fight with him till you have good arms. I shall be anxious till I hear from you.'

"'If I can,' said Geraint, 'I will let you hear from me by to-morrow afternoon.'

"'And one thing more, Geraint,' said the Queen, 'if you avenge this insult to me I shall never forget it, and when you bring a bride to our court, as such a noble young knight as you must do some time, I will dress her for her marriage as no bride in England was ever dressed before.'

"Then Geraint left the Queen and followed the knight and the woman and the dwarf. They crossed the Usk and passed King Arthur's castle, and then rode along at an easy pace for many miles. And at last they came to a town and they rode through the street. And as the knight and the woman and the dwarf passed along all the people ran out of their shops and houses to look at them. They waved their hats, those of them who had hats, and cheered till the knight had gone by, and then they all went back to their work, for they were all busy. Geraint saw that they were polishing swords and cleaning armor and shoeing horses, and acting quite as if they were getting ready for a war and were afraid of being too late. Geraint followed the knight up the street till he came—now what is all this trouble about?"

The train had stopped and a guard came up to our window. "This is Cardiff, sir," he said.

Now when you are getting out of a train and are telling a porter where he is to take your luggage and whether this is all of your luggage or whether there is some in the van, and if so, how much, you don't have a great deal of time left to tell stories to little girls. So the story was interrupted, and it stayed interrupted till we had gone to an hotel and given warning that we should want some dinner after awhile, and then had started out to take a little walk and to see the town.

After all there did seem to be some sense in Helen's mother's question about why we came to Cardiff. I don't mean any disrespect to the good town of Cardiff, only if we had been set down in St. Mary's Street without knowing how we came there, we should scarcely have known that we were not in New York. Cardiff is a fine city, a rich and a prosperous city; it is growing fast; there are good shops and houses, and the people look contented; but we did not need to come three thousand miles to see a street that looked like New York.

"And wasn't it most remarkable," I said, "that we should get to Cardiff just as I was telling you that Geraint got to Cardiff? And he had come all the way from Caerleon on horseback, too, and we came by train. But what a difference between the two towns! Then Caerleon was a great city, with castles and churches and strong walls and towers, and now it is a poor little country village, almost hidden and hardly known. Then Cardiff was a poor little town, perhaps not very much larger than Caerleon is now, and it has grown up while Caerleon has grown down, till it is this big handsome city, with shops and hotels and banks and railways and a harbor full of ships. I don't know whether Geraint rode up this same street where we are or not, but at any rate, as he followed the knight and the woman and the dwarf, he saw them ride into a castle. Now did you ever see anything so remarkable in your life?"

"'So remarkable as what?' said Helen.

"Why, don't you see this beautiful place in front of us? Isn't it remarkable that we should come to Cardiff Castle just at the very minute that I was telling you that Geraint came to it? I suppose the castle that Geraint saw and the one that we see would look about as different as any two buildings could and both be Cardiff Castle. Geraint did not go into the castle, but took the road toward the river, as we will do now, for the story has nothing to do with the inside of the castle. Yet there is another story that has something to do with it, and Geraint might have thought of it as he passed the gate and went on his way to find a place to stay for the night. But I don't suppose he did, because he does not seem to have known much about Cardiff. He probably did not know that this castle once belonged to Uther Pendragon, before King Arthur's time. I have read somewhere that it belonged to Arthur himself afterward and that Caerleon-upon-Usk was really Cardiff. But that is nonsense, because Caerleon was and is Caerleon.

"But Cardiff Castle did belong to Uther Pendragon, without any doubt. And in those same days there was a good old knight named Sir Cleges. He was rich once, but he entertained his friends so handsomely and gave so much to the poor that he found at last that he had scarcely anything left. He did not care for this so much for himself, but it made him sorrowful that he could not give any more to the poor.

"One Christmas Eve he was feeling more sad than usual, because that was the time in the year when he used to give the most and when he used to have the most of his friends about him. But his wife tried to cheer him and told him that he ought to be grateful that they still had enough for themselves to eat, though they had not much more. So Sir Cleges and his wife and their children sat down and ate what they had, and tried to be as merry as they could, and then they all went to bed.

"The next day they went to church. When they came home Sir Cleges went into his garden and knelt down under a cherry-tree and prayed and thanked God for all He had given him, whether it was much or little. Then, as he was an old man, he took hold of a low branch of the tree to help him in rising, and as soon as he took hold of it he saw that the branch was covered with leaves and cherries.

"He called his wife and showed her the wonder, and she told him that he ought to take the cherries to Cardiff Castle and give them to the King. You know there were no hothouses in those days, to raise fruits out of season, and there were no fast ships to bring tropical fruits to England. So at Christmas even a king might look at cherries as a good deal of a luxury.

"Sir Cleges took his wife's advice, picked the cherries, and carried them in a basket to the castle. He dressed himself like a poor man, as indeed he was. At the door of the castle stood a porter, who would not let him in at first. You would know just by that that it was not in King Arthur's time. No porter would ever turn any poor man away from King Arthur's castle. But when the porter saw the cherries in the basket he knew that the King would be likely to give something handsome for them. So he told Sir Cleges that he would let him in if he would promise to pay him a third of what the King gave him for the cherries.

" There was nothing for Sir Cleges to do but promise, so he promised. When he got to the door of the great hall he found an usher, and the usher told him he could not come in. Then the usher saw the cherries too, and, being just as good and faithful a servant as the porter, he also told Sir Cleges that he would let him in if he would promise him a third of what he got from the King for the cherries. And again Sir Cleges had to promise. Then he went into the hall, and the King's steward stopped him and would not let him go near the King, till he too saw the cherries and made Sir Cleges promise him a third of the pay for them. That made three thirds, so you see the prospect was that whatever the pay turned out to be, he was not going to have much of it left for himself.

" But now, at last, he came before the King and offered him the cherries. And the King was so much pleased that he promised to give him just whatever he should ask in payment. You see Uther Pendragon was not so careful

about making that kind of promise as Arthur
was. 'My lord,' said Sir Cleges, 'what I ask
is that you will let me strike twelve blows
wherever I like.'

"That is a very foolish thing to ask,' said
the King; 'I am sorry I let you choose; think
again; let me give you money or land, or a
horse or something that will do you some
good.'

"'You have promised, my lord,' Sir Cleges
answered, 'to give me whatever I ask. These
twelve blows are what I ask and you must
give them to me.'

"'If you will be a fool, then,' said the King,
'have your own way and go.'

"Now while this little talk had been going
on the steward had been turning all sorts of
colors and wishing he was out of his bargain.
And as soon as the King had told Sir Cleges
that he might have what he had asked, he
turned and struck the steward four good
blows with his staff. Then he went to the
door of the hall and treated the usher to his
four blows, and then to the door of the castle, where he gave the porter his third of the
pay.

"Then he started away from the castle, but
he had not gone far when a page came running
after him, to tell him that the King commanded
him to come back. Sir Cleges went back to

the hall and there he found an old minstrel
playing on a harp and singing about him to
the King. The minstrel had recognized Sir
Cleges at the very first, because he was one
of the many to whom he had been kind when
he was rich. So as soon as he had gone the
minstrel began to sing this song, which he was
clever enough to make up on the spot, to tell
the King who he was and what good things he
had done.

"So the King had sent for Sir Cleges to
come back, and when he saw him again he
too remembered his old knight. He made him
tell the whole story about the porter and the
usher and the steward, and he enjoyed the
story so much that he gave him Cardiff Castle
and a good deal more besides. Kings do
often enjoy jokes on other people. So Sir
Cleges was rich again, and I hope that this
time he did not give away everything that he
had, but I am afraid he did, for when Geraint
came here Cardiff Castle did not belong to Sir
Cleges or to anybody of his family, and it had
not in a long time.

"Speaking about Geraint brings me back to
the story. He rode along, as I said, toward
the river—this very road, I suppose, and certainly this very river—and he crossed a bridge,
just where this bridge is that we are crossing,
no doubt. And on the other side of the river

he saw an old palace. It was falling to pieces then, and it must have fallen all to pieces hundreds of years ago, so we cannot see it. An old man in poor clothes, that had once been rich, sat at the door. The old man rose and welcomed Geraint, and asked him why he came there. 'I am looking for a place to spend the night,' Geraint answered.

"'It is but a poor place that you will find with us,' the old man answered; 'but, such as it is, you are welcome to it. Come in.'

"And the old man led Geraint into the hall, and then into an upper chamber. And in the chamber was an old woman, dressed, like the man, in poor clothes that had once been rich. And beside her sat a young girl, in poor clothes too, but Geraint thought that he had never seen one more beautiful.

"Now I am sure I don't know what made me say 'but' just then. Her being in poor clothes was no reason why she should not look beautiful to Geraint or to anybody else. And I will stop right here to tell you a secret. It is a secret, because there are not half a dozen girls in the world who know it. The others may have heard it, but they do not believe it. It is this: If a girl or a woman is really pretty, she looks her very prettiest in the simplest and plainest dress that she can wear. If all the girls and the women in the world were to find that out all at once, it would ruin more people's business than if the Bank of England should fail.

"Well, while Geraint was looking at this girl and thinking that he had never seen one more beautiful, the old man said to her: 'Enid, there is no one to attend to this young man's horse but you,' and the girl went away to look after the horse.

"Perhaps you think that Geraint might have looked after his own horse, but that would never have done at all. When Geraint was their guest, this old man and his wife and their daughter would as soon have thought of turning him out of doors into a storm as of letting him take care of his own horse. They had no servant, and so one of themselves had to do it. And when she had given the horse corn to eat and straw for his bed, she came back, and then her father sent her to the town to get something for their dinner. By and by she came back with a boy, bringing meat and bread and wine.

"Then they cooked the meat and sat down and ate. That is to say, the old man and his wife and Geraint sat down, and Enid served them. And when they were done eating Geraint said: 'Tell me, if you will, who you are, and why you live in this strange old palace, and who owns it.'

"'I own it,' the old man answered, 'and I am Yniol, and I once owned the whole of the town yonder, and much more.'

"'Then might I ask you,' said Geraint, 'why do you not own them now?'

"'A nephew of mine,' the Earl answered, 'made war against me and took them all from me. They call him the Earl now, and he lives in the castle that you saw across the river. He has left me nothing but this one old house.'

"'And can you tell me,' Geraint asked, 'anything of the knight who rode into the town to-day with the woman and the dwarf, and why all the people in the town seemed so busy?'

"'He came,' said Yniol, 'for the tournament which they are to have to-morrow, and the people of the town are busy making ready for the tournament. They do this every year. In the meadow near the town they set up two forks, and across the forks they lay a silver rod, and on the rod they place a sparrow-hawk. The sparrow-hawk is the prize of the tournament. Every knight brings with him the lady that he loves best, and it is for her that he tries to win the sparrow-hawk. The knight whom you saw won it the last year and the year before. If he wins it again to-morrow they will send it to him every year, and he will not come to fight for it any more. To-morrow, when the sparrow-hawk is set up, he will say to the lady who is with him that she is the most beautiful there and the most worthy to have it, and he will tell her to take it. Then, if any other knight wishes to fight with him for it, he will say that the lady with him is more beautiful and that it belongs to her. And then they will fight to see who can win it.'

"You have noticed perhaps that these old knights used to fight, sometimes, about very small things. If one of them refused to tell another who he was or where he was going, that was quite enough to make a fight. If one of them simply wanted to fight, for no reason at all, the other was usually very obliging. If they both chanced to love the same woman, of course they fought about that, and if they loved different women, they fought about that too. That was one of the commonest reasons of all. One said that his lady was the most beautiful in the world, and the other said that his was. Then they fought. And the queerest part of it was that when they were done fighting both of them felt sure that the lady whose knight had beaten was really more beautiful than the other. And it was this kind of fight, it seems, that they had for the sparrow-hawk.

"Then Geraint told Yniol of the insult to Queen Guinevere and asked him to advise him what to do. 'It is not easy to advise you,' said the old man. 'It would be well if you

;ould fight with him in this tournament.   I
would gladly lend you such armor as I have
and my horse, if you like him better than your
own.   Yet I do not know how you can fight in
the tournament, because nobody can challenge
him except for the lady whom he loves best,
and she must be there with him.'

"Then Geraint said : ' I will take your armor
gladly, but I will ride my own horse, for we
know each other.   And when the time comes,
if you will let me challenge for this maiden
here, your daughter, I will promise that if I
am not killed in the tournament, I will love her
as long as I live, and if I am killed she will be
free, and no harm will have been done to her.'

"And the old man answered: ' I know that
you are an honorable knight, and if the maiden
herself is pleased, I shall be pleased too.'   And
the mother looked as glad as her husband, and
Enid turned away her head and did not say no.

"In the morning they were all in the meadow
outside the town, and all the people of the
town were there too.   And the knight whom
Geraint had followed the day before rode out
in front of them all and told the woman who
was with him to take the sparrow-hawk, because she was the most beautiful of all who
were there and the best deserving of it.   But
as soon as he said it Geraint rode forward and
cried : ' Do not take it ; there is one here who

is more beautiful than you and more worthy to have the prize!'

"And the other knight cried: 'If you think your lady more worthy of the prize than mine, fight with me to prove it!'

"Then they took their places far apart. Geraint wore Yniol's armor, and it was old-fashioned and rusty, and some of it was broken, and the other knight had the newest and best of armor, but Geraint remembered how the dwarf had struck him in the face with his whip, and he thought that he could fight the man in any armor or in none. So they rushed together and broke both their spears. Then Yniol gave Geraint a new spear and the dwarf gave one to the other knight. And they broke those too and many more. But at last one of Geraint's spears held, and his enemy was thrown from his horse's back upon the ground.

"Then Geraint sprang off his horse and drew his sword, and the other knight was up and ready for him. And now the old and poor and worn armor that Geraint had on was against him. When they were on horseback it was not so much matter, for then he caught the point of the spear on his shield. But now the armor was so heavy and rusty that he could not move and work in it easily, and it cracked with the blows of his enemy's sword, and links of the mail broke and fell off. He fought the harder because he knew this, and when he seemed to have a little the better of the fight, the old man called out to him and cheered him on. Then the other knight seemed to be fighting a little the better, and the cheers came from the young Earl and his friends.

"And both of them got little wounds, and blood and sweat ran down into their eyes, till they could scarcely see. They were both striking wildly, when the old man came to Geraint and said to him: 'Remember the insult to your Queen! You promised to avenge it! Do not let her hear that you were beaten and could not do it!'

"And when he heard that it seemed to Geraint that the Queen and her maiden, whom the dwarf had struck, were looking at him. They would soon know and be ashamed if he failed, and it was as if they were there to see him fail. And a stronger thought than this was that Enid really saw him, and he must not fail. And with all the strength that he had left he struck the knight upon the head and broke through his helmet, so that he fell to the ground with a great wound. Then the knight begged mercy of Geraint, and Geraint said to him: 'Your dwarf would not tell me who you were; tell me now yourself.'

"And the knight answered: 'I am Edyrn, the son of Nudd.'

"'You shall have mercy,' said Geraint, 'if you will go to Queen Guinevere and make whatever atonement she shall ask for the insult to her. Go now, and do not get off your horse till you are at the court of Arthur.'

"And Edyrn answered: 'I will go.'

"Now whether there was any more of the tournament after that I do not know. I don't see how there could be, unless some knight thought that his lady was more beautiful than Enid, and wanted to fight it out with Geraint. And surely no one of them did that. And yet it seems to me that, as it was, there was a pretty small tournament. If the knights came there intending to fight, why did they not fight with Geraint? And if they did not intend to fight, why was all that mighty polishing of swords and cleaning of armors and shoeing of horses that Geraint had seen in the town the night before? You see I mean always to tell you these stories so that you can understand them just as well as I do myself. But if the dear old poets and story-tellers, whom I never can love enough, told them in the first place so that nobody could understand them, it isn't my fault, is it? And so all that I can tell you now is that Edyrn, the son of Nudd, and his lady and his dwarf rode gloomily away toward Caerleon,

and that the young Earl came to Geraint and
begged him to come to his castle.

"But Geraint said that he would go nowhere
in that town but to the house of the old man,
where he had stayed the night before. So he
went home with Yniol and his wife and Enid,
and in the evening the young Earl came there
to visit him. And the young Earl brought
many of his knights with him and provisions
to make a great feast for all of them. And
when it was over the young Earl begged
Geraint again to come and visit him the next
day. And Geraint answered: 'No; to-morrow I must go back to the court of King
Arthur. And one reason why I must go is to
ask King Arthur to get back this old man's
possessions for him.'

"'You need not go back to him for that,'
said the young Earl. 'I will give him back
everything, if you ask it.'

"'I do ask it, then,' said Geraint, and the
young Earl kept his promise and gave back to
Yniol everything that he had taken from him.
Oh, they did love a good fighter in those days,
and there was nothing that he could ask of
them that they would not do.

"The next morning Geraint was ready to go
to Caerleon. And he asked where Enid was,
for of course she was to go with him. 'Her
mother,' said Yniol, 'is dressing her the best

she can, so that she may look fit to go to the court.'

" 'Tell her,' said Geraint, 'to wear only the gown that I first saw her in. For the Queen promised me that whenever I should bring a bride to the court, she herself would dress her for her marriage as no bride in England was ever dressed before.'

" So Enid came in her old, simple gown, and she and Geraint rode away.

" And now the story goes back to the morning when King Arthur and his knights hunted the stag. They had scarcely let the dogs loose and begun the hunt when the stag ran close to where Arthur was, and Arthur himself killed it and cut off its head. Now you remember that before the hunt the King had commanded that the head of the stag should be given to the one who killed it, to keep or to give to whom he pleased. As nearly as I can make out, this was an old rule, which counted only when one of the knights or squires killed the stag, and not when the King himself killed it. So on the way home they got into a little dispute about the stag's head and who should have it. I don't know why the King should not settle for himself who should have it, but it seems he did not, and they were still talking of it when they came to the castle.

" Then the Queen told them of the insult that

had been done to her and how Geraint had gone to avenge it. And she said: 'Let us wait till Geraint comes back, before we give the head of the stag to any one. It may be that he will deserve to have it better than any here.'

"And they all agreed. And the next day the Queen set a watch on the ramparts of the castle to look for Geraint. And in the afternoon the watchmen saw a dwarf riding toward the castle, and after him a woman, and last of all a knight, with his armor broken and covered with dust, riding slowly and hanging his head, as if in shame and grief. And one of the watchmen went to tell the Queen. 'It must be the knight whom Geraint followed,' she said; 'he has overtaken him and beaten him and sent him here.'

"Then Edyrn, the son of Nudd, came to the gate and into the hall. And he told the Queen and the King all that had happened at Cardiff and how Geraint had done and how he had sent him to offer atonement to the Queen. Then they gave Edyrn a room in the castle and sent the King's physician to cure his wounds, and again the men on the rampart watched for the coming of Geraint.

"And the next day the watchmen saw Geraint and Enid coming. And they told the Queen, and she called all her women and went down to meet Geraint and to welcome him. But when she thanked Geraint for fighting for her and defending her honor, he said: 'Thank this maiden here; I could not have fought for you if it had not been for her. I fought for you and for her together, and she is the bride whom you said that I should some time bring to the court.'

"'She is as welcome as you,' said the Queen, 'and I thank you both.'

"Then they all went to the hall, where the King was waiting for them, and he welcomed them and thanked them, too. And everybody said that Enid must have the head of the stag. And when Enid was married to Geraint, the Queen, as she had promised, dressed her as no bride in England was ever dressed before. Yet, if Geraint was the sensible fellow that I think he was, I believe that he thought her more beautiful in the poor and simple gown that she wore when he first saw her, and when he fought for her and won the sparrow-hawk, and when she rode with him from Cardiff and the poor old house of her father to Caerleon and the castle of the King."

CHAPTER VII

ON THE WRONG SIDE OF THE SEVERN

"What did we go to Cardiff for?" said Helen's mother.

"I have explained all that before," I said. "The mistake was not in going to Cardiff, but in choosing the wrong way to come from it."

The way that I had chosen to come from Cardiff was by a little steamer that was now taking us up the river Severn and across it to Bristol. I chose this way because of one of my rules for travelling. It is a good rule, too, and it is this: never go anywhere by land when you can go by water. But the best rules fail sometimes, and this time this one had failed utterly. For the steamer was small and not over-clean, it had no cabin and nothing to sit on but boards and boxes and barrels, and the water was so rough that the boat danced about in the most unpleasant way. As we got farther from the shore the water grew rougher still, and when-

ever the boat plunged into a wave the spray
dashed high up and came down all over the
deck. And it got worse and worse. Then we
found a little spot right in the middle of the
boat, behind the funnel and a pile of freight,
and there we sat on bags and coils of rope. It
was selfish in us, no doubt, to stay there, for it
was the only spot on the steamer where the
flying spray did not fall, and it was just big
enough for us three. But we thought that
since we had been lucky enough to discover
the place we might as well have it as anybody,
and it was not comfortable after all, only a little less uncomfortable than the rest of the boat.

" The trouble is," I said, " that we are on the
wrong side of the Severn."

" I don't know what you mean by that," said
Helen's mother; " I wish that we were safe on
either side. The trouble is that we are in the
middle of it."

" Not at all," I answered; "I mean that we
are on the top side of it, when we ought to be
on the bottom side."

" Ought to be on the bottom side! I am
afraid we shall be if it gets a little rougher."

" Yes, madam, I am told that there is a very
good tunnel under the river and that that is
one way to get from Cardiff to Bristol. I decided to come this way because I thought that
there would probably be more to see above the

river than under it. I am sorry now, because, though the bottom of the river may be darker than the top, it is probably smoother."

" Then it wasn't necessary to come on this horrible little boat ? "

" No ; it was a dreadful mistake. Still I do not think it was my fault that the larger boat needed repairing just at this particular time, so that they had to use this one."

" Oh, no, I suppose it wasn't; but only to think of all we are going through, and it wasn't even necessary ! "

" Madam," I said, " I feel what a wrong I have done much more than you can. To prove it, if you like, I will not try to guide you any more. I will give up our first agreement; you shall take charge of the whole journey, and I will go wherever you say."

And now I have a chance to show you what a truly great and good woman Helen's mother is, for she only answered: " Don't be silly; everybody makes mistakes sometimes."

" But it's too bad," Helen said, " to have to sit here and get bobbed up and down, with nothing but this dirty yellow water all around, and not even any places to tell stories about."

Then I began to cheer up, for such a direct challenge as this seemed really good and old-fashioned.

" Do you dare to think, my child," I said,

"after all the years that you have known me, that I cannot tell you a story anywhere I choose, by land or sea? And do you think that only the hills and the towns and the fields here in England have stories, and that the rivers have none? Why, how do you suppose this river came to be called the Severn at all?"

Helen did not seem to have any particular thoughts about it, but she looked at the river with a little more favor. "Once, long, long before King Arthur's time," I said, "there was a king of England named Locrin. It was not called England then. It was called Logris, after him, and when you are old enough to read very old books you will find it called Logris often. Now this Locrin was lucky enough once to conquer a king named Humber. While Humber was running away he got drowned in a river. Then they thought they could not do better than to name the river after him, and there it is, up in the other end of England now, name and all. So Humber fought and ran away, but did not live to fight another day.

"And besides some other things that Locrin captured from Humber he took a prisoner. This was a beautiful German princess, whom Humber had carried off, after he had conquered her father's country, and her name was Estril-dis. Locrin straightway fell in love with her and wanted to marry her, but he had already promised to marry the daughter of the Duke of Cornwall. Probably this promise would not have disturbed him much, but the Duke was very particular about it. The old priest who wrote this story and called it history, says that he brought a battle-axe with him when he came to talk with the King about it. Of course Locrin liked to have his own way as well as most people, but he was ready to listen to good arguments. So, when the Duke of Cornwall placed the matter clearly before him, he said he would marry the Duke's daughter, and he did.

" But the King had a palace made for Estrildis, all underground, so that she could never be found by the Duke of Cornwall or anybody else who might want to harm her. And after seven years the Duke died, and then the King divorced the Duke's daughter, brought Estrildis up out of the ground, and made her his wife and his Queen. And Locrin and Estrildis had a daughter, whom they named Sabre. Now of course the Duke's daughter did not like the way things were going, and after awhile she resolved to do something about it. She went back to Cornwall and told the people there how badly she had been treated, and she raised an army to go and fight the King of England. They did fight, and Locrin was killed.

" Then the Duke's daughter made herself

Queen again and ordered poor Estrildis and her daughter Sabre to be thrown into this great river that we are crossing. Then, from the name of Sabre, they called the river Sabren, and by some twisting or other that name has got turned into Severn."

"I don't think that is much of a story," said Helen.

"Perhaps it isn't," I admitted; "but you know we are not in a very good place to enjoy stories. Now what if I were to tell you a rather livelier story, with plenty of things in it that are hard to believe? Perhaps trying to believe them will make you forget how uncomfortable you are. At any rate I will try it.

"I have told you before that there used to be a great many little kings scattered all over England. One of these kings had a wife, with a hard name to pronounce, and a son. The story is not about the King or his wife, so their names do not matter. It is about the son, and his name was Kilhooch. When Kilhooch was still a child his mother fell sick and felt sure that she was going to die. She feared that after she was dead the King would marry again, and that her son would have a stepmother who would not treat him kindly. So she made the King promise that he would not marry till he should see a briar with two blossoms growing on her grave. Then she died.

" Seven years after the King rode hunting one day and passed near the Queen's grave, and saw that there was a briar with two blossoms growing on it. So, as he was getting rather tired of living alone, he at once found another wife, as kings never seem to have any trouble in doing. Kilhooch was getting to be a fine young man by this time, and almost the first thing that his step-mother said to him was that he ought to have a wife too. Kilhooch answered that he thought he was too young to marry. Then the step-mother said : ' I believe that you will never be pleased with any woman for your wife except Olwen, the daughter of Yspaddaden Penkawr.'

" Now I don't know why Kilhooch's step-mother told him this. It was not at all easy for a young man to get Olwen, the daughter of Yspaddaden Penkawr, and perhaps his step-mother hoped that he would be killed in trying to do it. You know step-mothers are almost always wicked, in stories. But then, she knew, too, how sweet and lovely Olwen was, and perhaps when she saw what a beautiful and brave-looking boy Kilhooch was, she thought that he was just the one who deserved such a wife, and that he would prize her all the more if he had a little trouble in getting her. I am quite willing to believe that this was her reason, because I never heard of her doing anything else that was bad. At any rate Kilhooch fell so deeply in love with the very thought of Olwen that his father asked him what was the matter. 'My step-mother says,' he answered, 'that I shall never find any one to please me for my wife except Olwen, the daughter of Yspaddaden Penkawr, and I do not know how I am to get her.'

"'That will be easy enough,' said his father; 'go to King Arthur and ask him to help you.'

"I don't suppose you would believe me if I told you how Kilhooch dressed himself and equipped himself and his horse and his dogs to go to the court of King Arthur. And yet you may as well believe whatever you hear about the way a very young man dresses when he is very much in love. There was gold pretty nearly everywhere, except where there was something better. The hilt of his sword was of gold, and around his body he wore a cloth of purple, with a gold apple at each corner, and each of them was worth a hundred cattle. His horse had a saddle of gold and his dogs had collars of rubies. He had two spears of silver, so sharp that they could wound the wind and make blood flow. And his horse stepped so lightly that it did not bend a blade of grass under its hoofs.

"When he came to Arthur's court he rode straight into the hall on his horse and said:

'King Arthur, I am Prince Kilhooch, and I have come to ask a gift of you.'

"'You shall have any gift,' said Arthur, 'that is in reason and is not against my honor or my kingdom.'

"'I ask of you,' said the young man, 'that you help me to get Olwen, the daughter of Yspaddaden Penkawr, for my wife. And I ask it, too, of all your knights.'

"Now this young Kilhooch was really a remarkable boy, for he knew the names of all Arthur's knights, and when he asked them to help him he named them all. I am not going to name the knights for you, partly because it would take too long and partly because I can't, but Kilhooch named them till I am sure everybody must have been tired of hearing him. And the old book where this story is written tells some remarkable things about some of the knights. I don't suppose you would believe them if I should repeat them for you. There was one of them who walked on his head, to save his feet. There was one who was so beautiful that in battle no one touched him with a spear, because all thought he was an angel, and there was another who was so ugly that no one touched him, because they thought he was a devil. There was one who could walk across a wood on the tops of the trees. Another could jump over three hun-

dred acres of ground, and still another could
stand on one foot all day.   There was one who
could beat a barn with an iron flail till all that
was left of it was as fine as the oats on the floor.
One could spread his beard over the eight and
forty rafters in Arthur's hall.   Two, the attendants of Guinevere, had feet as swift as their
thoughts when they bore a message.   But the
story does not say how swift their thoughts
were.   Another had ears so good that he could
hear an ant fifty miles off rise from its nest in
the morning, and one had eyes so good that he
could see a mote in a sunbeam the whole length
of England.   You can do just as you like about
believing all these things.   You know I told
you in the first place that some things in this
story might be rather hard.   I don't more than
half believe in these wonderful knights of
Arthur's myself, particularly because I never
heard of them except in this one story.

"But when Kilhooch had called on all of
them, together and separately, to help him to
get Olwen, the daughter of Yspaddaden Penkawr, the King answered him: 'I have never
heard of the maiden of whom you speak, but
I will gladly send men to search for her and
they shall find her for you if they can.'

"Then Kay said to the young man: 'Go
with us and we will not part till we find her,
and you shall have her.'

" Then Arthur called Sir Bedivere, one of his best knights, and Kyndelig, the guide, and told them to go with Kilhooch and Kay. This Kyndelig was just as good a guide in a country that he had never seen before as he was in his own. You see he was much better at the business than I am. He would never have brought you out in this little jumping boat on this dingy Severn, just because he had never seen it before. And Arthur told Gawain to go with them, and Goorhyr, who understood all languages, even those of animals and birds. And he sent Menoo with them, who could cast very useful spells over things.

" So, all together, they set out, and when they had travelled a long way they came to a great plain, and across it they saw a great, beautiful castle. It was morning when they saw it first and they thought that it was not far off, yet they went toward it till evening and then it looked no nearer than at first. And all the next day they went on, and all the next, and it was not till the evening of that third day that they found they were really near the castle.

" Then they came to a flock of sheep that covered the whole plain, as far as they could see, and on a mound sat a herdsman. His dress was made of skins, and beside him was a dog as big as a horse. Menoo cast a spell upon the dog, so that he could not hurt them, and then they went forward. 'Herdsman,' said Kay, 'whose castle is this?'

"'You are stupid not to know that,' the herdsman answered; 'all the world knows that this is the castle of Yspaddaden Penkawr.'

"'And who are you, herdsman?'

"I am Custennin, the brother of Yspaddaden Penkawr, and he treats me cruelly because I have great possessions, and he wants them. And who are you?'

"'We are the men of Arthur,' Kay answered, 'and we have come with this young man, Kilhooch, to find Olwen, the daughter of Yspaddaden Penkawr, that she may be his wife.'

"'Then go back to Arthur,' said Custennin, 'for no one who came here to seek Olwen ever went away again alive.'

"Then Custennin rose to go away, and Kilhooch gave him a ring, and he took it home and gave it to his wife. 'Where did you get this ring?' she asked.

"'From Kilhooch,' he answered, 'who has come to find Olwen and to marry her.'

"Then the knights themselves came to Custennin's house, and Custennin's wife ran out to meet them. And she was so glad to see them that she wanted to embrace Kay, who came first. But Kay, who was not usually very clever, happened to have a wonderfully happy

"Beside him was a dog as big as a horse."

thought just then. He picked up a log from a pile that lay near and put it in the woman's arms and she hugged it till the wood was all in shreds. 'If you had squeezed me like that,' said Kay, 'nobody would ever have loved me again.'

"Then the woman opened a chest, and out of it came a handsome young man. 'Why do you hide this boy so?' asked Goorhyr.

"'I hide him,' the woman said, 'because he is the only one that is left of my twenty-four sons. Yspaddaden Penkawr has killed all the rest, and I know he will find this one and kill him too, some time, in spite of all that I can do.'

"'Then let him come with me,' said Kay, 'and he shall not be killed unless I am killed too.'

"'Why do you come here?' the woman asked, though she knew already.

"'We come to seek Olwen,' Kay answered.

"'Then,' said the woman, 'go away before any one in the castle knows that you are here, or you will all be killed. They have all been killed who ever came before to seek her.'

"'We will not go,' said Kay again, 'till we see Olwen. Will she come here, if you send for her?'

"'Yes,' said the woman, 'but I will not betray her when she trusts me. I will not send for her unless you promise that you will do her no harm.'

" ' We promise,' they all said, so the woman sent for Olwen and she came. Now I know just exactly how beautiful Olwen was, but I am not going to tell you, because you would only laugh at me and tell me that the loveliest girl in the world is always the one that I happen to be telling a story about. Well, what of it ? Isn't that the way to tell stories? I will only tell you that clover grew up wherever Olwen stepped on the ground, and that as soon as Kilhooch saw her he loved her even more than he did before he saw her. And, having no time to waste, he told her so at once and asked her to come away with him.

" She did not seem at all surprised to hear him say that he loved her. I dare say she was quite used to it, though nobody had ever loved her before and lived. But she said: 'I cannot go with you yet, because I have promised my father that I will never be married till he says I may. You must go to my father and ask him, and whatever he tells you to do, you must do it. If you do not, you will never get me, and you will scarcely save your own life.'

" Now the reason why Yspaddaden Penkawr made his daughter promise never to be married without his leave was that it had been prophesied that he should die on the day when his daughter was married. That was why he set tasks that he thought were impossible for all the lovers who came to seek her, and that was why he killed them when they failed in the tasks.

"So they all went to the castle and stood before Yspaddaden Penkawr. 'We have come,' they said, to ask your daughter Olwen for this young man, Prince Kilhooch.'

"Yspaddaden Penkawr could not see them, because his eyebrows were so heavy that they had fallen down over his eyes. 'Where are my servants?' he said. 'Raise up the forks under my eyebrows, so that I may see what my son-in-law looks like. Is it you who want my daughter?'

"And Kilhooch answered: 'It is I.'

"'You must promise then,' said Yspaddaden Penkawr, 'to do everything that I ask, and when you have done all that I ask you shall have her.'

"'I promise,' said Kilhooch.

"'Do you see the land out yonder?' said Yspaddaden Penkawr. 'When I first met the mother of this maiden nine bushels of flax were sown there, and none of it ever grew. I require you to get back all the seed, so that it may be sown in new ground, that a wimple may be made from the flax for my daughter to wear on the day when she is married to you.'

" 'That will be easy to do,' said Kilhooch.

" 'Though you do this,' said Yspaddaden Penkawr, 'there is something else which you cannot do. For my daughter's wedding my hair must be cut and combed, and I must be shaved. My hair and my beard are so stiff and strong that this cannot be done except with the scissors and the comb and the razor that are between the ears of the wild boar Toorch Trooyth. He was a king who was turned into a wild boar for his wickedness. He will not give up the scissors and the comb and the razor of himself and you cannot take them from him.'

" 'That will be easy to do,' said Kilhooch.

" 'You cannot hunt Toorch Trooyth,' said Yspaddaden Penkawr, 'without the help of Mabon, the son of Modron. He was taken from his mother when he was only three days old and no one knows where he is now.'

" 'It will be easy to find him,' said Kilhooch.

" 'No one can find him,' said Yspaddaden Penkawr, 'except his cousin Eidoel. You must find Eidoel first and you cannot do that.'

" 'That will be easy to do,' said Kilhooch.

" 'Though you do this, there is something else which you cannot do. You must have the sword of the giant Goornach. He will not give it or sell it, and you cannot take it from him.'

"'It will be easy for me to get it.'

"'In all these things you will have labor and trouble. You will never do them and you will never win my daughter.'

"'King Arthur will help me in all these things and I shall win your daughter.'

"'Go, then,' said Yspaddaden Penkawr, 'and when you have done all these things come back to me and you shall have her.'

"Then Kilhooch and the knights who were with him and the son of Custennin left the castle of Yspaddaden Penkawr and travelled far, till they came before the largest castle they had ever seen. They went to the gate and knocked. 'Whose castle is this?' said Goorhyr.

"'It is the castle of the giant Goornach,' the porter answered.

"'Can we come in?' said Goorhyr.

"'No,' said the porter, 'the knife is in the meat and the drink is in the horn and there is revelry in the hall, and no one can come in to-night except a craftsman who brings his craft.'

"'Then I am a craftsman,' said Kay.

"'What is your craft?'

"'I am a burnisher of swords.'

"'I will tell the giant Goornach,' said the porter, 'and bring you an answer.'

"So the porter went to the giant and told

him that there were some men at the gate who wanted to come in, and that one of them said that he could burnish swords. 'Bring him in,' said the giant; 'I have wanted some one for a long time to burnish my sword.'

"So Kay was let in and the giant's sword was brought to him. And Kay took out a whetstone and polished half the sword. Then he gave it to the giant and asked if it pleased him. 'It is well done,' said the giant; 'make the rest of it like this.'

"And when Kay had finished polishing the sword he said: 'It is the scabbard that has rusted the sword. Give it to me, so that I can take out the old wooden sides and put in new ones.'

"And the giant gave him the scabbard, and as he stood close to the giant, as if he were about to put the sword into the scabbard, suddenly he struck the giant with it and cut off his head with one blow. Then Kay left the castle, and he and Kilhooch and the others went to King Arthur and carried the sword of the giant Goornach with them.

"They told Arthur all that they had done, and when he had heard the story he said: 'Which of these things that we must do for Prince Kilhooch will it be best to try first?'

"'We cannot hunt Toorch Trooyth,' they said, 'without the help of Mabon, the son of

Modron, and we cannot find him without his cousin Eidoel.'

"Now Eidoel was a prisoner in the castle of Glivi. But Glivi gave him up to Arthur as soon as he asked for him, and then Arthur went back to his own castle and left the rest of them to find Mabon, the son of Modron. And why they should go first of all to the Blackbird of Cilgoori I don't know, but they did. And Goorhyr, who understood all languages, you know, said: 'Blackbird of Cilgoori, do you know anything of Mabon, the son of Modron, who was taken from his mother when he was three days old?'

"And the Blackbird answered: 'There was an anvil here when I first came, and I was a young bird then. Nothing has touched that anvil since then except my beak, with which I have pecked at it every morning. And now there is scarcely so much left of it as the size of a walnut. Yet in all that time I have never heard anything of Mabon, the son of Modron. But I will lead you to the Stag of Redynvre. He is older than I.'

"And when they found the Stag Goorhyr said: 'Stag of Redynvre, we are an embassy from King Arthur. Tell us if you know anything of Mabon, the son of Modron.'

"Then the stag answered: 'When I came to this place there was no tree here, but only an oak sapling. That sapling grew to be a great oak, and it lived its life and died, and now there is nothing left of it but a stump, yet in all that time I have never heard of Mabon, the son of Modron. But I will lead you to one who is older than I.'

"So they went with the Stag and he led them to the Owl of Coom Cawlwyd. And Goorhyr said: 'Owl of Coom Cawlwyd, we are an embassy from King Arthur. Tell us if you know anything of Mabon, the son of Modron.'

"'When I came to this place,' said the Owl, 'this wide valley which you see was covered with a wood. Men came and rooted it up and another wood grew, and the one which is here now is the third, yet in all that time I have never heard of Mabon, the son of Modron. But I will take you to the oldest animal in the world, the Eagle of Gwern Abwy.'

"So the Owl led the way, and again Goorhyr said: 'Eagle of Gwern Abwy, we are an embassy from King Arthur. Tell us if you know anything of Mabon, the son of Modron.'

"And the Eagle answered: 'When I came to this place there was a rock here so high that I could perch on the top of it and peck at the stars. It has been worn away now till it is scarcely a span high, and I have never heard of Mabon, the son of Modron. Yet, once, when

I was looking for food, I saw a great Salmon.
I tried to catch him, but he dragged me under
the water and I scarcely saved my life. Then
I and many other eagles went to attack the
Salmon and to destroy him, but he made peace
with me and I took fifty fish-spears out of his
back. He travels much, and he may have
heard of Mabon, the son of Modron.'

"Then they all followed the Eagle, and he
led them to this same river Severn, and they
found the Salmon of Llyn Llyw. And the
Eagle said: 'Salmon of Llyn Llyw, I have
brought to you an embassy from King Arthur,
to ask if you know anything of Mabon, the son
of Modron.'

"And the Salmon answered: 'Sometimes I
go up this river as far as Gloucester. There
stands a great castle, and in a dungeon I have
heard wailing and groaning. Let two of you
stand on my shoulders and I will take you
there, and you can see and hear for yourselves.'

"So Kay and Goorhyr stood on the Salmon's
shoulders and he swam with them up the Severn to Gloucester. And there they found the
castle, and from the dungeon, just as the Salmon had said, came a sound of some one groaning and lamenting. Then Goorhyr called out
and asked who it was in the dungeon, and the
voice in the dungeon answered: 'I am Mabon,
the son of Modron.'

"'And can you be released from this prison,' Goorhyr asked, 'for money or for gifts or by fighting?'

"'If I am ever released,' the voice answered, 'it must be by fighting.'

"Then Kay and Goorhyr went back to their companions, and they all went to King Arthur and told him where Mabon, the son of Modron, was. Then Arthur called his warriors and they went and laid siege to the castle. And while the men of the castle were busy fighting with the army in front, the Salmon took Kay and Bedivere to the back, and they broke through the wall and took Mabon, the son of Modron, out. Then, as they wanted nothing more, Arthur and his army went home."

"And what did that cousin of Mabon's have to do with it?" Helen asked. "I thought he had to help them somehow."

"I am sure I don't know," I had to admit. "Yspaddaden Penkawr told them that they could not find Mabon, the son of Modron, unless they found Eidoel first, and so they found him. But the story does not say that he did anything afterward, more than all the rest of them did. I rather think that Yspaddaden Penkawr tried to think of as many things as he could for his son-in-law to do, just to make his task long and hard. And I am not sure that they could not have hunted Toorch

Trooyth just as well without Mabon, the son of Modron, himself."

" I shouldn't think," Helen suggested, " that he would be any better hunter than anybody else, if he had been in prison ever since he was three days old."

" I shouldn't think so either. But perhaps there was some sort of magic, some charm, about having Eidoel and Mabon, the son of Modron, with them, whether they really did anything or not. All I am sure about is that the story says they had to have them and they did have them. And about the time that they got Mabon, the son of Modron, out of prison, another very lucky thing happened. One of Arthur's knights saved a hill of ants from being burned, and the ants were so grateful that they said they would do something for him that no man could do. So they went and picked out of the ground the nine bushels of flax-seed that Yspaddaden Penkawr had told Kilhooch he must get for him. The ants came and piled up the flax-seed till there was only one seed missing, and a lame ant brought that one before night.

" It was time now to begin the hunt of the wild boar Toorch Trooyth. He was said to be somewhere in Ireland, and Arthur first sent Menoo, the man who could cast spells, to see if he really had the razor and the comb and the scissors that Yspaddaden Penkawr wanted between his ears. Menoo, it seems, could cast spells upon himself just as well as upon anybody else, so he changed himself into a bird. Then he found the den where Toorch Trooyth lived, and there, sure enough, he saw the razor and the comb and the scissors between his ears. Menoo hovered over him and tried to snatch away one of them, but he only got one of the long, stiff bristles, and then the boar got up angrily and shook himself, and Menoo flew away and went back to tell Arthur.

"Then Arthur called all his warriors together and they crossed over to Ireland to hunt Toorch Trooyth. It may have been a great punishment for this wicked king to turn him into a wild boar, but it does not seem to have made him any less wicked or any less dangerous, for the first day that they hunted him, the story says that he laid waste the fifth part of Ireland. They hunted him and fought with him there for eleven days altogether, and then he ran into the sea and started to swim across the channel toward England. And he swam straight toward the mouth of this same river Severn, and came to land somewhere in Devonshire, where we are going as fast as we can get there.

"Now it would do no good for me to tell you, even if I could remember, all the places

where Toorch Trooyth led Arthur and his
men in their hunt. It lasted for many days,
and the wild boar rushed through the country, trampling down and destroying the crops,
killing cattle and dogs and killing some of Arthur's men too. And at last Arthur resolved
that he would surround him with as many of
his knights as he could and force him into the
Severn. So they came up with him and
pressed upon him all around, and forced him
into the river, and while he was there Mabon,
the son of Modron, who was on one side of
him, snatched the razor from between his ears,
and a knight of Arthur's, on the other side,
seized the scissors. But before they could get
the comb the boar broke away from them and
got back to the land.

"Then he ran and none of them could overtake him again till he came into Cornwall.
There they did overtake him, but just here the
story-teller gives it up and does not try to tell
us what happened 'in the fight. But he does
tell us that all that had gone before was mere
play compared with it. But they got the
comb and then they drove the boar into the
sea, and he swam away, and after that nobody
ever knew what became of him.

"Then Kilhooch took the razor and the scissors and the comb to Yspaddaden Penkawr, and
he could not deny that Kilhooch had done

everything that he had told him to do, so he had to give him his daughter Olwen for his wife. And on the day when they were married Yspaddaden Penkawr died, as it had been foretold that he would, and nobody was sorry, because he had killed so many young men who had come to marry his daughter that everybody thought it was time for him to die. And yet I am afraid that Kilhooch was never truly sorry for all the young men who had been killed because they could not do the things that Yspaddaden Penkawr asked of them. And they might have done them, too, just as well as he, if they had had King Arthur to help them, like him."

The water all around us had grown wonderfully smooth and the boat was going along quietly and right side up. We stood up to look around and see what had made the change. "How narrow the river is here!" Helen said.

"Yes," I said, "we must be off the Severn now and on the Avon; not the Stratford Avon, but the Bristol Avon."

CHAPTER VIII

THE PATHS THAT ENID RODE

I AM glad that my fathers of two hundred and fifty years ago came from Devonshire. If I could have chosen the place for them to come from, I could not have found a better one. It does not matter just where we went on our way through Devon. One part of it is as beautiful as another. Everywhere you see the same gentle slopes of hillsides, covered with the same rich, green depth of velvet grass. Everywhere the same contented-looking sheep are feeding in the sunny pastures or lying sleepily in the shade. On the hills and in the fields of grain are scattered the same red and yellow flowers. Along all the roads are the same green hedges, higher than your head on both sides, often, as you walk, as high as your head even, sometimes, when you ride. All these things are the same in their sweet and peaceful loveliness, and yet they are all different, always fresh, always new. You never get tired of these scenes. The more you see of them the more you feel rested and refreshed and grateful.

And then they feed you so well in Devonshire. For those sheep are just as good to eat as they are to look at, and there are other things equally good to eat that do not show so much in the landscape. But the cows help the landscape, and the table too, because you owe all your clotted cream to them. When you are in Devonshire you get clotted cream with your orange marmalade or your strawberry jam, or whatever you have for breakfast; you get it again with your gooseberry tart for luncheon, and again with whatever comes at the end of your dinner. If you want to eat it on your bread at any time of the day, when you have bread, you can. In Devonshire they would no more think of asking you to eat a meal without clotted cream than without a knife and fork.

And while we were in Devonshire—I don't remember just where, but somewhere and somehow—I happened to say: "This Devon was Geraint's country. His father, Erbin, was the ruler of it, under King Arthur. But when Geraint had been at the court of Arthur for some three years, Erbin began to feel that he was getting too old to keep such order and peace as Arthur wanted everywhere. The great lords all about him knew that he was getting old too, and they thought that he would soon be too weak to defend his lands, and that then they could get some of them for themselves. So he sent messengers to Arthur to ask him to let his son Geraint come back and help him to defend the country and learn to rule it after him.

" Arthur was sorry to lose Geraint, for he had come to be one of the best knights of the court, but he knew that he was needed more in Devon, and he told him to go. So Geraint and Enid left Caerleon, and many of Arthur's best knights went with them to the Severn, and crossed over to the other side, and there Erbin's knights met them. Then they all went together to Erbin's court, and there was great rejoicing over Geraint's arrival. And as soon as it was over Geraint began to help his father in the ruling of the country. And with a strong and vigorous and resolute young man like Geraint at the head of affairs, one who could tell a troublesome lord what to do and then make him do it, things were soon in better order than they had been, and there was no part of Arthur's kingdom that was better governed than Devon.

" Then, since there was no more real fighting to do, Geraint began to fight in tourna-

ments, as he had done at Arthur's court, and to
hunt with the other knights.   He was the best
of them all in these things, and his fame spread
all about the country.   But after a time Geraint began to get a little tired of tipping other
knights over in sham fights.   It was not at all
strange that he should, I think.   The wonder
to me is that they did not all get tired to death
of knocking one another over their horses' tails
and denting one another's helmet, and splitting
one another's shield.   And Geraint was sensible enough to care more for his wife than he
did for punching holes in his friends' armors,
so he stayed with her a good deal and began
to neglect the tournaments.

"But a good many people have got into
trouble by knowing more and being more
sensible than the people around them, and so
it was with Geraint.   For the knights were not
content with knowing that Geraint was the
best of all of them; they wanted him to be
proving it all the time.   They got to saying
that he was losing his courage, and that it was
a shame for him to stay at home with his wife
instead of winning more fame in the hunt and
the tournament.   Now this was just the way
that pretty nearly a hundred people out of a
hundred in those days would look at it, and it
was just the way that Erbin looked at it when
he heard this kind of talk about the court.   So

he told Enid of it, and asked her if it was she who had made Geraint give up all the sports in which he had been so famous and lead such a lazy life at home.

"And Enid looked at it just as Erbin did, and she said : 'No, indeed, I would never keep him away from any honor that he could win. I do not know why he does not go to the tournaments any more, but I am as sorry for it as you.'

"Now you know very good people are always getting it into their heads that they have done something dreadfully wrong, and it was just so with Enid. The more she thought about it the more she was afraid that it was her fault after all. She liked to have Geraint with her, of course, and so she feared that she had kept him with her when he ought to have been with the other knights. And one morning Enid sat watching by Geraint while he slept. She was gazing at him and thinking how beautiful and strong he was. Then she thought so hard that she thought out loud, and some tears came into her eyes, and one of them dropped on his face, and she said : 'Have I been doing so very wrong, and is it my fault that all his strength is wasted and that they do not call him the bravest of all the knights any more?'

"And the tear that fell on his face awakened him, and he heard a part of what she said. And what he heard and the tears that he saw made him think one of the most insane things that such a good, sensible fellow as he could possibly think. I am afraid I cannot tell you exactly what it was, because I don't think either of us is insane enough to understand it. But, as nearly as I can tell you what he thought, it was like this : seeing the tears made him think that Enid was unhappy ; then he concluded that she must be tired of staying with him at his lonely little court of Devon, away from the great court of Arthur; and hearing her say something about doing wrong made him think that she had done something very dreadfully wrong, and as she was crying over him, he thought that the whole wrong and unhappiness must be about something that concerned him. Now did you ever hear of anything more absurd? If he had been fully awake I don't believe that he would ever have thought of any such nonsense. But as it was these mad notions got into his head while he was only half awake. Then they stayed there, and it was a long time before he got fully waked up, as you will see presently.

"But just now, being only half awake, as I prefer to believe, he ordered his horse and he ordered Enid's horse, and he put on his armor. Then he said to Enid : 'Put on your worst riding-dress and come and ride with me, and you shall not come back here till you see whether I am as weak and as cowardly as you think.'

"I don't wonder that poor Enid was surprised, and that she answered: 'I do not know what you mean or why you ask me to do this.'

"'It is not time for you to know yet,' Geraint said.

"And when they were on their horses he said: 'Ride forward and keep a long way ahead of me. Do not turn back and do not speak to me unless I speak to you first.'

"And so they rode away. It was a different sort of ride from that one they took side by side on that day when they came toward Caerleon, and the watchers on the rampart saw them far off, and Queen Guinevere came down to welcome them, and King Arthur waited to meet them. Now Enid was sad and perplexed with wondering what it all meant. She could not think where they were going, or why, and she could not understand why Geraint would not let her speak to him. And Geraint was more troubled than she, for he himself, I believe, did not know just why he was doing this silly thing. He must have known that his own thoughts were all wrong, even though he was only half awake.

"They must have ridden, I think, in some of the very places where we have been. They did not look the same then, perhaps, but the

story says that in one place the road was between two hedges. That was like what we
have seen, surely; yet in most places I think
that the ways were rougher then and that
there were more woods.   The woods were
dangerous, too, because there were a good
many thieves in them, in spite of all that King
Arthur and Geraint had done to drive them
out.

"And as Enid rode along so far ahead, she
saw four armed horsemen come out of the
woods near her. And she heard one of them
say: 'Here is a chance to get two horses and
an armor; that glum-looking knight there can
do nothing against us.'

"Then Enid tried to think what she ought
to do. Geraint had told her not to speak to
him, yet she feared that if she did not warn
him the four men would set upon him all at
once and kill him. Of course she did the only
sensible thing that anybody could do. She
turned back and warned him. And what do
you think he said? 'I told you,' he said, 'not
to speak to me. No doubt you would like to
see these men kill me, but I am not afraid of
them.' Now do you believe, Helen, that Geraint could ever have said that if he had been
more than half awake?

"But he was awake enough to run his spear
through the first of the four men who came

against him. And then he served each of the
other three in the same way in his turn. Then
he took off the armors of the four men and
bound them on the backs of the four horses.
And he tied the bridles of the horses together
and mounted his own horse again and said to
Enid : 'Drive these horses before you and
keep far ahead of me, and do not dare to speak
to me again unless I speak to you first.'

"So they rode on again, but Enid did not
have so much time now to wonder what it all
meant, because she had to attend to driving
the horses. And by and by they came out of
the wood and began crossing a plain. In the
middle of it was a clump of trees, and out of
this came three men, armed and on horseback.
As Enid came near them she heard one of them
say : 'This is lucky; here are four good horses
and four good armors and that knight there
with the hangdog look cannot prevent our taking them.'

"Then Enid thought, just as she had thought
before, of what she ought to do, and she did
just what she had done before and warned Geraint. And he, being still, as I believe, only
half awake, was angry with her again for speaking. Yet he charged against the men and overthrew them all, as he had done before. And
then, just as he had done before, he took the
armors and bound them on the backs of the

horses and fastened the bridles together and told Enid to drive the horses before her with the others.

"Then on they went across the plain till they came near another wood. And this time five horsemen came out against them. And just the same things happened that had happened twice before. Enid warned Geraint and he was angry with her for speaking, yet he overthrew the men. And this time Enid had five more horses to drive before her, so that there were twelve in all."

Just here Helen, who had been looking doubtful for some time, refused to believe any more. "How could she drive twelve horses," she asked, "without any reins or anything at all to drive them with?"

"It is not very easy to understand," I said, "but we must remember that they had good horses in those days and they were well trained. They must have been, or they would not have done their parts in those jousts and tournaments. The horses often got knocked down, as well as the men, and the horses must have known it. So it must have taken good training to make one of them charge straight against another with a knight on his back, knowing that there was going to be a dreadful shock and a crash, and that as likely as not he and his rider were both going to be thrown over backward. And it is said that those horses used to be trained so that they would gallop straight against a stone wall, if their riders told them to do it. So you see horses in those days were taught to go just where they were told to go. No doubt Enid did have hard work to drive these twelve, and the story says that she did, but it was not so hard as you might think. If they had been as unreasonable as Geraint was, I am sure she could not have done anything with them at all. But horses are almost always more reasonable than men.

" Well, riding in this way, they came into the wood, and before they were through the wood it was night. So they turned out of the road and tied their horses to trees and slept. And very early in the morning they awoke and mounted and started again on their way. Soon they were out of the wood and in an open country. There was a great meadow, with mowers, on one side, and before them they saw a town. Then they met a boy who carried a basket and a large pitcher. ' Whence do you come?' said Geraint to the boy.

"' From the town yonder,' the boy answered; ' and whence are you?'

"' We have just come through the wood,' answered Geraint.

"' But you cannot have come through the wood this morning,' said the boy.

" ' No,' said Geraint ; ' we were in the wood all night.'

" ' Then you have had nothing to eat this morning,' said the boy ; ' will you take what I have here? It is the breakfast for the mowers, bread and meat and wine, but I can bring more for them.'

" Then Geraint thanked the boy and got off his horse. And the boy helped Enid off her horse, and then he served them while they ate. They must have been really hungry, for, as far as the story shows, they had eaten nothing that morning or the day before. ' And now,' said the boy, ' I must go and get something for the mowers.'

" ' As you go to the town,' said Geraint, ' find the best lodging for me that you can, and take any one of these horses that you like and the armor on his back, to pay you for your trouble.'

" So the boy went to the town and found the best lodging he could. But it did not seem to him that it was good enough for such a great lord as Geraint must be, so he went to the palace of the Earl, who was the lord of the place, and asked him what he should do. ' Tell the knight,' said the Earl, ' to come here to my palace, and I shall be glad to welcome him.'

" But when the boy brought the message to Geraint, he would not go to the Earl's palace, but only to the lodgings that the boy had found for him. And when they were there Geraint

told Enid to stay on one side of the room and
not to cross to the other side, where he was.
You see he had waked up this morning only
about as far as he did yesterday morning.

"Then the Earl sent word to Geraint that
he would come to visit him, and in the evening he came. And the Earl asked Geraint why
he was making this journey. 'To seek adventures,' said Geraint, 'and to go where I please.'

"And when the Earl saw how Enid stayed
on the other side of the room, all alone, he
could not understand it, any more than you
and I do, or any more than Enid and Geraint
themselves did. But the Earl was fully awake
and he saw how absurd it looked better than
Geraint. And since she kept so far away from
Geraint and neither of them spoke to the other,
the Earl thought that she must be going with
him for some reason against her will. So the
Earl said to Geraint: 'May I speak to the
maiden yonder, for I see she is not with you?'

"'Speak to her, if you like,' said Geraint.

"Then the Earl crossed the room to where
Enid was and said to her: 'It must be unpleasant to you to ride through the country with
this man. You have no house and you must
sleep in such places as you can find. You have
no servants and you must grow weary of riding all day, with no company but him. My
men are here with me. If you say the word

we can kill him in an instant, and then I will marry you and you shall come to my palace and you shall have everything that you want as long as you live.'

"But Enid answered: 'No; I would rather be on the roads and in the woods with that man than in your palace with you.'

"'Take care, then,' said the Earl; 'you are both here in my town, and here are my men. If I like I can kill him without your leave, and then I can make you marry me.'

"Then Enid was afraid that he would do as he said, so she answered him: 'Do not touch him yet; go away now, but come back to-morrow and kill him, if you will, and take me away, as if it were by force.'

"So the Earl went away and took all his men with him. And after awhile Geraint lay down and went to sleep. But Enid kept awake and watched. And by and by she took all Geraint's armor and placed it together, so that it should be ready for him to put on. Then she watched again till midnight. And at midnight she went to Geraint and spoke to him and woke him and told him all that the Earl had said. And again he was angry with her for speaking to him, but he called the man of the house and said to him: 'Take the eleven horses and the eleven suits of armor for your pay, and show us the way out of the town.'

"So they mounted their horses again and the man showed them the way and they left the town. And they rode on through the dark woods and between the dark fields till morning. And Enid still rode far ahead, as she had done on the first day. And when it began to grow light they saw a wide valley before them, and a river, with a bridge across it, and a town beyond. Soon they met a knight, and Geraint asked him whose town it was before him. 'It belongs,' said the knight, 'to the Little King.'

"You know I have told you something about some little kings before. I called them little kings because they amounted to so little. This one was called the Little King because his body was so little.

"Geraint kept on his way and soon he met another knight. His horse was big, but Geraint thought that the knight was the smallest man he had ever seen on a horse. 'What are you doing here,' the knight cried out to Geraint, 'and why do you come into a place that belongs to me?'

"'I did not know that this road was forbidden,' said Geraint. 'Who are you, and why should I not come here?'

"'I am the Little King,' the other answered, 'and I let no one pass here unless he fights with me.'

"It was not at all uncommon in those days,

when a knight could not possibly find anything else to fight about, for him to take up
his stand somewhere and declare that no other
knight should pass without fighting him. Wandering knights always expected to find such
fixed knights as these, now and then, and they
were always ready for them. So Geraint said
no more, but closed his helmet and put his
spear in rest. Then they fought for a long
time, first on horseback and then on foot. And
Geraint thought that he had never had a
harder fight, not even with Edyrn, the son of
Nudd. For the Little King was so small that
it was hard to hit him, but he struck back as
often and as strongly as any knight. Yet at
last Geraint drove his sword out of his hand
and brought him to the ground, and the Little
King begged him to spare his life. 'I will give
you your life,' Geraint answered, 'if you will
promise never to fight against me again, but
to be ready always to come and fight for me,
if you hear that I am in trouble.'

" And the Little King promised, and Geraint
and Enid rode on their way. And still Enid
rode ahead and wondered what this long,
dreadful journey was for and why she might
not ask. And as they came to another wood
they heard a sound of someone crying, and
Geraint said: 'Wait here till I see what is the
matter.'

"And when he left the road and went into the wood he found a woman sitting beside a knight who lay dead upon the ground. And when Geraint asked her what had happened, she told him that the knight was her husband and that three giants had killed him. 'And which way did they go?' Geraint asked.

"'They went yonder,' said the woman, 'by the high road; but do not try to follow them, or they will kill you as they killed my husband.'

"Then Geraint went back to Enid and told her to go to the woman and to stay with her, while he followed the giants. And Enid went, and she forgot all her other sadness and her wonder about the journey that she was on, in her fear that Geraint would not come back.

"But Geraint followed the giants. In a little while he came upon one of them and thrust him through with his spear, so that he fell down dead. And so he served the second, when he came up with him, but the third struck him with a club that he carried and split his shield and crushed his shoulder. Yet Geraint killed him, too, and then turned back toward the place where he had left Enid. The pain in his shoulder was so great that he could scarcely bear it till he came where Enid and the other woman were, and when he did reach the spot he fell down off his horse in a swoon.

"Just then the Earl who was lord of that part of the country was passing with some of his men, and the women called to them for help. And the Earl came and ordered a few of his men to bury the dead knight, but he did not know whether Geraint was dead or not, so he had him carried to his castle, and he took the two women there too. They put Geraint on a couch in the hall, but they did no more for him, for the table was there, spread with food and wine, and they cared more about that.

"They were a rough crew, the Earl and his men, and they shouted and laughed and ate and drank, as if there had been no one near who felt any sorrow. And as soon as Enid came into the hall the Earl dragged her to the table and told her to eat too. 'I cannot eat,' she answered, 'and I will never eat till that man who lies there shall rise and eat too.'

"'Drink, then,' said the Earl, and he poured some wine for her.

"'I will not drink,' she answered, 'till he rises and drinks, too.'

"'Do not be so sad and silly,' said the Earl, 'about one man. You were his wife, were you? Well, then, he is dead, and that is the end of him. You shall stay with me now and be my wife. Drink now.'

"'I shall always be sad,' said Enid, 'if he is dead, and I cannot eat or drink.'

"'I have tried to be gentle with you,' the Earl cried out, 'and it is of no use; now I must be rough with you; you shall eat when I tell you and drink when I tell you!' and then he struck her on the face.

"Then Enid gave a great cry. It was not so much because she was hurt, but because she thought that Geraint must be really dead. For she thought that if he had been alive the Earl would not have dared to strike her. Now I don't know whether Geraint had heard anything of what the Earl and Enid had said. I hope so, for it was just what he ought to hear. But he surely heard her cry and he waked up then. He waked up fully, too, not half. And he either heard or saw exactly how things were, and he seized his sword, which had been left near him, and rushed upon the Earl and struck him dead with one blow. And all the rest of the men in the hall were frightened and ran away, for they thought that a dead man had risen up to punish them.

"And Geraint, as I said, was all awake now. He looked at Enid and saw and felt how faithful and good she was, how little she could do any wrong, and how much she loved him. And

he felt ashamed of himself for being so foolish
and so cruel. He did not say a word, but he
took her hand and led her out of the hall. He
found their horses and they mounted and rode
away, and now they ride side by side.

"And soon they saw spears over the hedges
that hid the road, where it curved, and then
they heard horses and knew that armed men
were coming. They waited, and in a moment
they saw many men on horseback and a knight
at the head of them. When he came a little
nearer they knew him, and it was the Little
King. 'Is it Geraint?' he cried. 'I heard
that you were in trouble, and I was coming to
help you.'

"Then, when the Little King found that
Geraint was wounded, he made him and Enid
come to the castle of a baron near by who was
his friend. There they all stayed till Geraint
was well, and then he and Enid went home, and
the Little King went with them. And Geraint
went back to the tournaments and the hunts,
and as long as he lived there were few knights
so good or so famous as he. But there was
something better about Geraint than that. For
he had learned how foolish it was, when he
might wake up and find that everything was
right, to stay half-asleep and dream that everything was wrong. And Enid was so happy to
see him as he used to be that she never asked

him why he made her take that long, weary
ride and keep ahead of him and never speak to
him. And Geraint was so happy, too, and he
knew so well that Enid could do no wrong,
that he never asked her what she had said or
what she had meant or why she was so sad on
that morning when her tears fell and half-
awoke him."

CHAPTER IX

A LITTLE JOURNEY IN CORNWALL

It is not easy to remember just where you have been in Cornwall. It does not matter where we started, and I could not possibly tell you what way we went on the day that I mean to tell you what I can about. My memory is all confused. I do know that I asked the man who sold us our railway tickets whether we should have to change anywhere. He said that we must change at Such-a-place. I don't dare to say how many times it turned out that we had to change before we got to Such-a-place, or how many times after we left it. I will not tell you a lie, and if I told you the truth you would not believe me.

But I remember that we saw many of those pretty slopes of pastures, such as we had seen in Devon, and I remember that we saw something else that was not so pretty. This was a tall, narrow, dingy house, like a house in a toy village, and a tall chimney. We saw these over and over again, and somebody told us that wherever we saw them there was a mine. There were mines in Cornwall hundreds of years before King Arthur's time. The Phœnicians knew of them long before the Romans came. And the Romans knew how rich they were, and that was one reason why they liked England. Now they are rather neglected and many of them are not worked at all.

" I don't know at all where we are," I said, as we got into a new train, after one of our many changes, " but if we have not passed it I think that there is a strange little lake not far from here. We shall not see it to-day, for I think there is no railway very near it. It is a lake that has wonderful stories about it.

" It happened once that Arthur had left the court and had gone out alone to fight with a knight who had taken his place at a certain well and made every other knight who passed fight with him. You know I told you that they sometimes did that. In the fight Arthur's sword had been broken. It was not the sword that he drew out of the stone to prove himself the true King. That one he had given to Gawain, if I remember rightly.

" Then Merlin met him, and when Merlin saw that he had no sword he said to him: ' My lord, I know where there is a sword near here that you may have, if you will come and take it.'

"So Arthur followed Merlin. He led him a little way to the foot of a hill and then up the hill. It was a steep place to climb, and when Arthur came to what he thought was the top, there was as much more of the hill still before him. Higher and higher he went, till he saw the very crest of the hill just ahead and nothing beyond it but the sky. He could not guess where Merlin was leading him, but just as he reached the highest place and thought that there would be a gentle slope for him to go down on the other side, he stood still in wonder. For there before him was no slope of a hillside, but a broad lake. He stood upon the very edge of it when he saw it first, and he heard the little waves plashing on the shore at his very feet.

"It was strange enough to find a lake like this on the very top of a hill, but about this one there were yet stranger things. Some people said that there were fairies who lived in this lake, and some said that there were evil spirits. There are people who say so still. Arthur did not know of this, yet he might have guessed it for himself. No one could look out upon this water, as he did, and not feel that it was something wonderful. He could not see the other side or tell how broad

it was, though it was clear day all around.
For there were strange, bright, silvery mists
floating upon the water. They were moving
and shifting, so that for an instant the King
thought that he could catch just a glimpse of a
shore beyond, and then they closed across it
and he saw nothing but the shining, vapory
veil. Now the bright fog seemed rising and
growing thinner, till he looked at the ripples
of the water far from where he stood, and now
again it dropped down and he could see scarcely more than the waves that came against the
bank at his feet. The sun shone over it and
through it all, and the water, wherever he could
see it, gleamed like a polished armor, and the
mist dazzled his eyes like a light cloud with the
sun behind it at noon. He could see nothing
that was alive but Merlin, standing by his side,
and a bird like a sea-gull wheeling in circles
above the lake.

"Merlin said nothing, but pointed out upon
the lake, and the King looked that way. Then,
through a rift in the mist, he saw something
rising from the water. He could not make out
the form of it at first, but in a moment a little
puff of wind blew the vapors away from it and
he could see it better. Then he saw that an
arm rose out of the lake. The arm was covered with white silk and the hand held a sword
in a scabbard. The hilt of the sword was set

with big, rich jewels. As the sunshine touched
them, they shot out little rays of changing
light, red and purple, and green and orange,
and, when the fog closed around it a little more,
the sun still made the beautiful hilt glow and
light up a little of the cloud around it like a
dim torch.

" The King was still gazing at this wonder
when Merlin touched him and pointed again
out upon the lake in another direction.   There
Arthur saw another form, and this one moved.
It came nearer to them and he saw that it was
the form of a woman walking on the water.
Merlin whispered to him : 'She is the Lady of
the Lake ; the sword is hers, but she will give
it to you if you ask it.'

" So, when she came near them, Arthur said :
' Lady, is that your sword out there upon the
lake?'

" ' Yes,' she answered, 'it is mine.'

" ' You see I have no sword,' said Arthur;
' will you give me that?'

" ' Yes,' she answered again; ' go into the boat
there and row out and take it.'

" Then Arthur saw a little boat by the shore
close to him, though he had not seen it before.
He got into it, and so did Merlin.   Merlin took
an oar, but he scarcely seemed to touch the
water with it, and the boat went quickly away
from the shore and stopped close to the sword.

Then Arthur took the sword, and the arm and the hand that held it went down under the water. Merlin just dipped his oar again and the boat went back to the shore. They stepped out of the boat and Merlin said : 'Draw the sword and look at it.'

"So Arthur drew the sword and the blade of it shone like a mirror. 'The name of the sword is Excalibur,' said Merlin; 'but tell me now whether you like the sword or the scabbard better.'

"'It is a beautiful scabbard,' the King answered; ' but surely anybody must like a sword better than a scabbard.'

"'You are wrong in that,' said Merlin; 'it is a wonderful sword indeed—the best sword in the world—yet the scabbard is better. For the man who has that scabbard by him can never be killed in battle, and, though he may be wounded, his wounds will never bleed and he will lose none of his strength. So guard them both, but more than anything else that you have guard this scabbard.'

"As they turned to go down the hill again Arthur looked back once more at the lake. All the mist was gone from it and it looked like any other lake. The water sparkled in the sunlight that shone all over it, and Arthur could plainly see the other shore across it and not very far off, and away beyond it a mountain with two peaks. The Lady of the Lake was gone and there was no boat. Everything about it was changed except the bird like a sea-gull, that wheeled in great circles high up in the air, and the soft lapping of the little waves against the bank and the strangeness of the lake's being there on the hilltop."

Have you ever travelled in a strange country, with nothing to guide you but books and maps and time-tables? If you never have I advise you to try it. If the strange country happens to be Cornwall, I advise you also to stick to your books and maps and time-tables and not to trouble yourself about what the people of the hotels and the railways tell you. If the way you want to go happens to be the way they want you to go, it is all very well. But if it doesn't, then they will tell you that the way they want you to go is the only way there is. I have said that I do not know just where we went in Cornwall that day, but I do know that after a time we got to Wadebridge. I know, too, that it was luncheon-time.

We were trying to find Tintagel, and one of my books said that a stage-coach went there from Wadebridge every other day. I had asked a railway man if there was a coach from Wadebridge to Tintagel and he said that there was not, but I did not believe him. He said

there was one from Bodmin. But I was resolved to go from Wadebridge. It might not
be the right day for the coach, but we could
stay till it was. If it proved that there was no
coach at all we could get a carriage. So,
against all advice, we came to Wadebridge.
The first man we saw was a railway man—a
porter. " Is there a coach from here to Tintagel?" I asked him.

" No, sir," he said ; "there is one from Bodmin."

I hated Bodmin by this time, so I made up
my mind that we would go by carriage. We
walked out of the station and there stood an
omnibus from an hotel. I thought I would try
once more. " Is there a coach that runs from
here to Tintagel?" I asked the omnibus
driver.

" Yes, sir," he said.

I cheered up at once. " Does it go to-day or
to-morrow?"

" Every day, sir."

" Ah, indeed, and at what time?"

" You've just about time to catch it, sir."

This was luck indeed. "And where does it
start from?"

"From our hotel, sir; get right in and I'll
take you there."

When we got to the hotel the coach had not
come and the proprietor thought that we would

have time for luncheon. We thought it was worth trying, so they brought us the cold lamb and the bread and the marmalade and the Devonshire cream, for there is as much Devonshire cream in Cornwall as there is in Devonshire. Before we were done with these we heard the coach-horn outside. But there was plenty of time, they said, for the coach did not go on again at once, and so it proved.

The coach was pretty full already, but the guard found places for us up behind, near his own seat. We were rather glad afterward that we could not get any better places, because the guard proved to be very pleasant company. I asked him why it was that the railway men had told us that there was no coach from Wade-bridge to Tintagel. "Why, you see," he said, "this coach is owned by the other railway. The Bodmin coach belongs to their railway."

I have told you all this so that when you go to Cornwall you may have your eyes open. Yet, after all that I have said, you must not expect to find any coach running between Wade-bridge and Camelford. The guard told us that they were building a railway to take the place of it, and no doubt it was done long before this time. I ought to say, too, right here, that the most of the people whom we met in Cornwall treated us honestly and most kindly. They did all that they could to make our visit among them pleasant, and we shall always remember them most happily and gratefully.

Here was this very guard, for instance, trying to amuse us with stories. " Do you see those two rocks off there?" he asked.

Yes, we saw them.

" They call those the Devil's Jump," he said. "They tell the story that the devil tried to jump over them once, and couldn't do it. So he never got any farther into Cornwall than that. And that is why there are so many saints in Cornwall, for all the parishes from here to the Land's End are named for saints."

" I have heard a different reason," I said, " for the devil's keeping out of Cornwall."

" Yes, sir?" he said, with an upward turn of his voice that meant : " I should be glad to hear the reason, if you care to tell me, sir."

" Why, I have heard," I said, " that the people in Cornwall make pies out of so many different things that the devil will never come here, for fear they should make a pie out of him."

I knew that Camelford, near where we were going now, pretended to be the real Camelot, and I tried to find out if the guard had anything to tell us about King Arthur. He did have something to tell that surprised me.

" Oh, yes," he said, " King Arthur lived here at Camelford, and the battle where he was

killed was fought here. There is a bridge that
they call Slaughter Bridge, where they say he
was killed, and there is a stone near by, with
some letters on it, where they say he was
buried."

All this was so new to me that I did not
know at all what to say. "Was King Arthur
killed in a battle, then?" Helen asked.

"Really," I answered, "I don't quite know.
He fought a great battle at last and was
wounded, and some said that he was killed.
Others believed that he was carried away to
the beautiful island of Avalon, to be cured of
his wounds. And there the old story-tellers
said that he was living still, and that sometime, when England was in great danger, he
would come back to fight again and to save his
people. But I did not think that that last
great battle was here."

"Yes, sir," said the guard again, "they will
show you Slaughter Bridge, where he was
killed, and the gravestone close by."

We did not go to Camelford village that
day. The coach took us to the Camelford railway station, and the guard told us that the village was two miles off. Neither did we have
time to find Slaughter Bridge and King Arthur's gravestone, but we resolved to look for
them some other time. At the station we had
to leave the coach and take a carriage for

Tintagel. It was a big, long affair, of the sort that we call a drag. I don't know what they call it in England, but I rather think they call it a drag too.

As soon as we had left the station everything around us seemed to change. Before the roads had looked like the Devon roads. There were the same green hedges along both sides of them, so high, sometimes, that sitting there on the top of the coach we could not see over them. Now, instead of the green hedges, there were gray walls of slate. But they were almost as pretty as the hedges—prettier, sometimes, we thought, for a change. For their color was a soft, warm gray, and grass and little flowers, yellow and blue, grew in the chinks between the stones, and now and then a scarlet poppy, glowing like a big ruby in the sunlight, stood straight up on the top of a wall, as if it wanted to catch the fresh breeze blowing in from the ocean better than it could down in the field.

The whole country about here is made of slate. Sometimes our way was between two great piles of it, built up with smooth sides toward the road, so that we seemed to be riding between two huge castles. They were so high that we could see nothing over them and nothing beyond them where the road curved. Here the coach-horn was no mere ornament or toy. As the carriage went dashing along the narrow road and whirling around the curves the driver blew clear notes on the horn to warn anybody ahead of us that we were coming. For if another carriage, going at the same rate as ours, had met us without warning as we turned one of those quick corners, it would have been worse than the crash of two lines of knights in a tournament. For we had no iron clothes on, and we were not used to it. There were some other things, too, that looked just dangerous enough to make us feel a little happier. These were the great holes filled with water, where slate had been taken out. There was one of them by the side of the road that looked like a harmless sort of puddle where the children might sail their boats, but the driver told us that it was a hundred feet deep.

And so it was a pleasant ride, but it was not long, and in a little while we were rather sorry to get to Tintagel. It is a bit of a village, just a few houses ranged along the two sides of a street. There are three or four large houses and two of them are hotels. To be more exact, they are two parts of the same hotel—the Wharncliffe Arms. It was something of a surprise and much of a pleasure to us to find in such a tiny place as Tintagel that the hotel was large and well kept, and good in every way.

But there was something else that made me like Tintagel as soon as I saw it. For it is perched on a high plain, with the strong, sweet air of the sea blowing freshly and freely over it. I always feel a gladness when I come near the ocean, for I feel that I am with an old friend. I feel more at home when I am near it, and I am sure we were all at home there at Tintagel as soon as we caught the sweep of that wind coming off the water and over the cliffs and over the fields. And had we not good cause to feel at home here? Was not this the same ocean that we had loved so long, the same by the side of which we had sat so many times, Helen and I, telling and hearing stories? The same ocean, but different sides. The rising sun shines on our side of it, and the setting sun on this. That is all.

CHAPTER X

WHO THE KING REALLY WAS

WE did not go to see the castle of Tintagel till evening. There were two or three reasons. It was getting a little late in the afternoon when we reached the village, and we were a little tired after our journey. But the best reason was that it is always better, when you can, to see ruins for the first time by moonlight. There was a good moon to-night and I knew that our first view of the castle would be a good one. " Many people who come here," some one had said to us at the hotel, "are disappointed because there is so little left of the ruins. They seem to expect to see something like Kenilworth. They ought to remember that this castle has been going to ruin a good deal longer than Kenilworth, and that it has to stand the terrible storms of this rough coast."

" I don't believe we shall be disappointed in the least," I said, as we walked through the village toward the shore and the castle. "I feel here more than I have felt anywhere else that we are in King Arthur's own country. I don't think that he ever lived at Tintagel at all, though they call it King Arthur's castle. Before his time Tintagel Castle belonged to the Duke of Cornwall. And so it does now, only now the Duke of Cornwall is the Prince of Wales, too, and then he was not. And after that it belonged to Mark, the King of Cornwall, who was as false and crafty and cowardly as Arthur was true and noble and brave. Yet this really was Arthur's country, and it seems to me that this rugged coast and these cliffs that for thousands of years have stood against the power and the fury of the ocean, and this free, open sky, are more worthy of King Arthur than anything else that I have ever seen in England.

"Everything here can remind you of him, if you look at it rightly. Why, look up into the sky itself. At home we see the same stars that we see here, but some of them have different names. Those up there above our heads we call the Lyre, but here they are Arthur's Harp. And there is our old friend the Dipper, but here we must call it Arthur's Chariot."

We had left the village by this time and were going up over a grassy hillside. In a few minutes our path brought us to the gate of the

castle.   We stopped to look at it a moment before we went in.   Before us was a piece of low,
ruined wall, with a gate-way in it.   It had been
arched once, but now one side of the arch was
all gone and there was just enough left of the
other side to show what the shape of it had
been.   Right up above this, and above us, on
our left hand, rose a high rock, and on that a
wall, worn and battered and beaten away indeed, and still crumbling, but even now heavy
and thick and strong-looking, even now scowl-
ing down at us, as if it would have us know
that it cared nothing for war or storm or time.

" Do you see," I said, " what a strong place
this must have been?   See how that piece of
wall stands up above everything and looks out
over everything.   Try to think of it as higher
still, with a rampart on its top, and then think of
a tower above that.   The castle has only this one
little gate on the side toward the land.   If any
enemy came against it, it must be by this road
that we have come, and from the top of that
wall every one who came could be seen I don't
know how far off.   They had no big guns then
to shoot at a castle miles away.   They had ma-
chines to throw stones, and they could shoot arrows, but it was easier to shoot them down than
up, and I think the men on the walls of a castle
like this must have been a good deal better off
than any men down below who might happen

to be attacking them. Then, if the enemy got near enough, they had only to drop stones, instead of throwing them. They used to pour down boiling water from the walls of castles, too, and drop other things that made it unpleasant for anybody who happened to be in their way.

" Now let us come in through the gate and see how the castle looks on the side toward the water. No, I don't think anybody would ever try to attack it on this side. Look across this chasm and see the other part of the castle, up there on the rocks. That is all but an island over there. See how the rocks stand almost straight up out of the ocean, and how high above it the castle is. Hear the waves crashing and pounding away down below there, and then try to think whether any one would have an easy time coming against Tintagel by sea. They say that this chasm was narrower once, and there was a bridge across from this part of the castle where we are to the other part, over there on the island. Suppose, then, that the enemy should batter down this wall. All that the people of the castle would have to do would be to cross over to the island and throw down the bridge, and what could any army in the world, without cannon, do against them then? As long as food held out I would much rather try to hold this castle than try to take it.

"Do you think this is too long a lecture about old-fashioned war? Well, you see, I want to make you feel what a wonderful castle this is as much as I feel it. And yet its strength is not what makes it seem so wonderful to me. It is the stories about it. Those are the wonderful places, after all, I think—the ones that have wonderful stories about them. It was so many years ago that I heard of Tintagel first, and I have read so much about it since then, that I can scarcely believe that at last I am really standing in Tintagel Castle. I have to stop and tell myself that it was just here—here— where we are this moment, that Arthur—but I have not told you that story yet, have I?

"Do you remember how, long ago, when we used to see stories in the fire, we sat on the shore one night and looked at a moon just like this one, and at a sea very different from this one? Do you remember how we saw a ship coming from the island away off in the darkness toward us and toward a castle on the shore? Do you remember, too, the knight who was on the ship and the princess whom he was bringing to be the wife of his King, and how they drank the magic love-potion together and always loved each other as long as they lived? Well, it was this very castle of Tintagel that we saw that night. This was the very sea that they sailed across. The island, which we could

see then, being three thousand miles away, but
which we cannot see, now that we are here,
was Ireland. The knight was Tristram and
the princess was Isolt. The King was King
Mark, of Cornwall, Tristram's uncle, who lived
here at Tintagel. I told you then that King
Mark seemed to me as kind and generous
a man as you could wish, but I told you, too,
that some time you might find out that he was
a very wicked man—mean, cruel, and treacherous. You see, I sometimes disagree with
myself a little, because I am telling different
stories. You can believe whichever story you
like. As for myself, I find no trouble in believing both of them.

"Now look along this shore, there to the
southwest, as far as you can see. The shore
reaches down there, a good deal farther than
you can see, to the Land's End. It was not the
Land's End in those days, for out beyond it a
rocky country stretched into the sea, as far as
where the Scilly Islands are now. That was
Lyonnesse, Tristram's country. Tristram's
father was the King of Lyonnesse and his
mother was the sister of King Mark. Now
Lyonnesse is all gone—sunk under the ocean
and lost—all but those rocks standing out there
alone, far off from any other land, the Scilly
Islands. Tristram was one of those knights
whom I have told you of who would rather be

knights of Arthur than kings in their own lands. Yet at the time I am telling you about now, Tristram was not a knight of the Round Table or of Arthur's court, but he was afterward, and while he lived he was the best knight of the world after Lancelot."

There is a carpet of grass, with patterns of blue and yellow flowers, all over the court-yard and in all the halls and rooms of Tintagel Castle. We sat down on the carpet, in a spot where a piece of wall sheltered us a little from the wind, and listened to the restless rumbling and dashing of the waves down in the little bay below us. Yes, ruins are best by moonlight. In the clear, sharp light of day they are like the skeletons of old, long-dead times. They are seen too plainly. It is so easy to know what they are that it is hard to think what they were. But in the dim half-light of the moon they are not the bones any longer, but the spirits, the ghosts of other days. Then your fancy can build up the walls and halls and towers again and bring back their people to them. To-morrow, here where we sit, there will be people laughing and talking and making sketches and taking photographs, and there will be every-day sights and sounds. To-night we have the place to ourselves, and there are no voices but our own and no other sounds but those of the sea, which were here always.

And so, for me, these walls rose around us
again, higher and stronger and statelier. Again
there were towers above them that looked far
over the land and over the sea. The grass
was gone and the court-yard had a floor of
stone. The castle spread out wider, too, as
well as higher. Even old rocks of the coast,
that long ago fell, with the wear of the wind
and the waves, down into that boiling depth,
came back and stood fast to hold the castle
walls. The gorge was narrower and the bridge
that led over to the island was in its place
again. Then, all at once, the court-yard filled
with armed men. The little door where we
had come in was barred and barricaded against
an enemy. There was a sound of horses' hoofs
on the pavement, and men were watching from
the ramparts and the tower. There was a
woman, too—the Duchess of Cornwall. She
climbed up to the tower and looked out
over the land to see if the Duke, her husband, was coming. And even before she
looked for him he had been killed in battle
and he would never come back. Yet she saw
three figures coming toward the castle that
were so like the Duke and two of his men
that she ran down to meet them and the gate
was opened for them. But it was all enchantment, their looking like the Duke and his
men, and so the gate, that they never could

have opened for themselves, was opened for them—

"What makes them call it King Arthur's castle," Helen asked, "if he never lived in it?"

"Well, that is a story that I suppose I must tell you. Once, when Arthur was at Caerleon-upon-Usk, there came to visit him Queen Ygerne. She had been the wife of Uther Pen-dragon when he was King of England. And she brought her daughter, Morgan-le-Fay. 'Le Fay' means 'the fairy,' and they called her that because she knew so much about magic. She did not know anywhere near so much about it as Merlin did, of course, but she knew a great deal. She was the wife of King Urien and the mother of Uwain, who, you know, was one of King Arthur's knights. She was very beautiful, and, I am sorry to say, very wicked.

"But the story is not about her. Arthur received Ygerne and Morgan-le-Fay, of course, as he ought to receive a queen and a princess who was the wife of a king and so a queen too. But there was one knight in his court who did not like to see such honors paid to Ygerne, even though she had been Queen of England. This was Ulfius, and he spoke to the King, before all the people in the hall, and said that it was wrong to do honor to this woman, for she was not worthy of it. 'Ulfius,' said the King, 'do you know what you say? Do you not re-

member that this woman was King Uther's
wife and that you were his knight? Have you
no more loyalty than this?'

"'I know, my lord,' said Ulfius, 'what I say,
and I tell you that this woman is not worthy
to come into your hall. When she was King
Uther's wife she had a child, a son, who would
have been King of England after Uther died.
But she deserted her child—sent him away
from her as soon as he was born. She never
knew whether he lived or died—never cared—
and so all those years before you came to us,
my lord, England had no king. Was not this
wickedness enough? I will prove what I say
against any one who cares to fight for her.'

"Then the King looked at Ygerne and she
answered: 'What he says is partly true, my
lord, but not all. I did lose my child and
never knew whether he lived or died, but I did
care. How does he dare to say that I did not
care? Does he think it was easy for me to let
my child go away from me and never come
back? I am a woman and I cannot fight with
him, but there must be some brave man here
in your court who will fight for me. I will
swear to him that I did nothing wicked in this
that Sir Ulfius charges.'

"You know that was another of their queer
ways. I have surely told you about it before.
Anybody could accuse anybody else of any-

thing he liked, as long as he was willing to 'prove' it, as they called it, by fighting. Then the one who was accused, or someone else for him, must fight with the accuser, and the whole question was settled, guilty or not guilty, by the way the fight went.

"'There shall be no fighting yet,' said the King, 'but Ulfius shall tell us more of what he has to say against you and you shall answer him. Ulfius, you have always been a good knight to Uther Pendragon and to me. You would not say these things, I know, if you did not believe that they were true. So tell us all that you know, that I may judge between you and this woman.'

"'My lord,' said Ulfius, 'long ago this Ygerne was the wife of Gorlois, the Duke of Cornwall. Once she came to King Uther's court with him, and the King loved her. He loved her so much that he made war against Gorlois, so that he might kill him and marry his wife, this Ygerne. Then Gorlois, to keep his wife and himself safe from King Uther, shut her up in the castle of Tintagel and shut himself up in another castle that he had, called Terrabil. Uther laid siege to the castle of Terrabil. Gorlois came out to fight with him and was killed in the battle. Still his wife was in the castle of Tintagel, and we could not hope to take that. It was too strong and there were

too many good knights in it with her. Merlin
was King Uther's friend then and I went to
find him to ask if he would help the King. I
found him and brought him and he went into
the King's tent. I do not know what he said
to the King.'

"'Then do not try to tell,' said the voice of
some one close to King Arthur. It was Merlin himself. He came before the King and
stood there and looked at Ulfius, in the way
he had when he meant to manage things himself just as he pleased. And you know that
when Merlin meant to manage things he always did it. 'I will tell you what I said to
King Uther,' he went on. 'I said to him that
he should have Ygerne for his wife, if he
would grant me one thing. He promised that
he would grant me anything. "Then promise
me," I said, "that when you and your new
Queen have a child, you will give him to me to
bring up as I choose," and he promised it.
Then I told him that I would make him look
like Gorlois; that I would make Ulfius look like
Brastias, who was one of the Duke's knights
then, and myself like Jordans, another of the
Duke's knights; that so we would go to Tintagel and they would let us in. Now, Ulfius,
tell us what was done next.'

"'What was done next?' said Ulfius; 'why,
by some of your enchantment, Merlin, you

changed us as you have said. You made King
Uther look like Gorlois, and me like Brastias,
and yourself like Jordans. We came to Tintagel and they opened the gate for us and
then——'

"'Let Queen Ygerne tell the King what
then,' said Merlin. 'It is time for her story
now.'

"'My lord,' Ygerne said, 'it is hard for me
to tell you. I thought that he was my husband,
Gorlois, at first, and when I heard that Gorlois
was dead I scarcely knew or cared what happened. But King Uther's men and the Duke's
men—my men—said that it would be best for
me to be married to him. My own men said
that if I was not he would still make war on us,
and it was nothing to me then what happened.
And so we were married. And what must I
tell you now, my lord?'

"'Tell now about the child,' said Merlin.

"'The child? Yes,' Ygerne answered. 'He
was taken away from me as soon as he was
born, as Ulfius has said. But it was King
Uther himself who took him away, and he gave
the child to a servant and told him to go to
the gate of the castle and give him to the poor
man who was waiting there. And the servant
came back and said that the poor man had
taken the child away. I do not know why
they took him.'

" ' They took him,' said Merlin, ' because I told them to do it. King Uther had promised the child to me. And now, Sir Ulfius, what if this young prince had been left with his mother? King Uther died soon after that. You know what the lords and the kings were in those days. What would have happened to a baby King of England? Would they not have killed him before his mother's eyes? You know they would. But I saved him from that.'

" Then Merlin turned to the King and said: ' My lord, I was that poor man who stood at the gate. I took the child away with me. We left the shadow of the castle walls and came out into the clear moonlight. We came out into the sea wind too. We could hear it humming and whistling around the castle. But it was not a common wind. For I could hear something more. I could hear sweet little voices in it. They came nearer to us and gathered around us. They were the voices of fairies. I could hear what they said, and so could the baby in my arms. But the baby forgot it all. Babies always forget what they hear and see and think. If they did not, grown up men would know some strange things. But I remembered. One of the fairy voices said: " Let us watch around this baby and guard him and help him to grow up to be a good man." And another said: "He shall be the truest of knights some day; this gift I give him." And another said: "This gift I give him: he shall be the noblest of kings." And another said: "He shall be generous and brave; these are my gifts to him." And at last a fairy voice said: "He shall live till he has made many better and happier; and after he is dead they shall bless him." And the wind died away and the voices died away.

"'And I carried the child, my lord, and gave him to a faithful knight of Uther's, Sir Ector, and told him to keep him and to care for him as if he were his own son.'

"When the King heard the name of Sir Ector it surprised him more than anything else he had heard. 'Where is Sir Ector?' he said.

"'I am here, my lord,' Sir Ector answered, coming and standing before him.

"'What did you do with this child?' the King asked.

"'I kept him, my lord,' the old knight answered, 'as Merlin told me, and I cared for him as if he had been my own son.'

"'Sir Ector,' said the King, 'I have always known you for the truest man in England, and I have known you as if you were my own father. Yet how can this be? I have been with you all these years and there were no

"They came nearer to us and gathered around us."

sons in your house but Kay, who is now my
seneschal, and I. What did you do with that
child? Where is he now?'

"'He sits there, my lord,' Sir Ector answered,
'on the throne before me.'

"Then at last Arthur saw it all, as you saw
it, no doubt, some time ago. He was the baby
who heard the fairy voices and forgot them.
He was the son of old King Uther Pendragon
and Queen Ygerne. He came down from his
seat and took his mother in his arms, and then
he led her to the throne and made her sit down
upon it by his side. And Ulfius came and
knelt before them and said: 'Forgive me,
my lord; I thought that what I said was
right.'

"And Arthur answered: 'We know you
thought that you were right, but guard well
what you think and what you say. My
mother and I forgive you.'

"I have never read of anything that Ygerne
did or of anything that happened to her after
that. But you see that the castle of Tintagel
is called King Arthur's castle, not because he
lived here, but because he was born here."

CHAPTER XI

SOME LITTLE ADVENTURES OF LANCELOT

WE went to the castle the next morning to see how it looked by daylight. "I suppose I ought to tell you before we get any farther," I said, as we took the road toward the shore again, "that when King Arthur found out that he was the son of King Uther Pendragon, he found out one or two other things. Queen Bellicent, the wife of King Lot, of Orkney, was the daughter of Gorlois and Ygerne, Arthur's mother. Perhaps you remember and perhaps you have forgotten that Queen Bellicent was the mother of Gawain, Gaheris, Agravain, and Gareth, so that all these were King Arthur's nephews. Then Queen Morgan-le-Fay, the wife of King Urien, was the daughter of Ygerne, too, and so Uwain was King Arthur's nephew. These are just some little family affairs that it may be convenient to know."

When we reached the castle we went in again through the broken doorway and stood looking out upon the sunny sea and away along the rocky coast, with its steep headland after headland, and down into that pit below us, where the waves seem to be always rolling and tumbling over the rough, broken rocks, even when they look calm out at sea. " There are wonderful things about this castle," I said, " besides that King Arthur was born here and that King Mark lived here and that Tristram brought Isolt here. The castle was built by giants, it was said, and when it stood here in all its strength and glory it used to be invisible on two days of every year. One of these days was Christmas and the other was in the summer. It was Midsummer Day, I suppose, though the story does not say so. Perhaps you think the most of the castle is invisible now. Perhaps you are right, but every stone of it disappeared then, and the only way the people who lived near it could tell where it was on those days was by certain other things that they knew were in a line with it, just as a fisherman knows how to find a spot on the water where he has found good fishing."

We had not gone close to the other part of the castle, over on the island, yet, and we thought that it was time we did. So we

scrambled down the steep side of the hill, half-
walking and running, and half-slipping and
sliding, till we got into the road at the bottom
of the ravine. Then we had to go to the
house where they kept the key of the castle
and borrow it. This keeping of keys to lend
is a beautiful plan. They lend one to anybody
who asks for it, and so you may not see at first
why they should not leave the door open and
let everybody go in without the key. It is because when you bring the key back there is a
very good chance for you to give a little tip
to the old woman who keeps it, and so, I suppose, she gets a fair living, and goodness knows
how she would get it if she did not have the
key of the castle to lend to people.

We knocked at the door of the old woman's
house and asked her if she had the key, just as if
we had not read the sign outside that said she
had. She gave us the key and told us to put
it into the lock upside down, to lock the door
again after we had gone in, and not to bother
about the people who were already there, because they had another key. Then we went
down the narrow path along the rocks, across
the little neck of land to what they call the
island, and up the rocks on the other side till
we came to a wall, with ramparts and a little
door, where we had to use our key. It was a
beautiful, old, romantic-looking wall, and we

stopped to admire it before we went in. We
thought that it was by far the finest part of the
castle that we had seen yet. We found out afterward that it was built only about fifty years
ago. They built it just so that they could
have a door in it, so that they could put a lock
on the door, so that they could have a key to
the lock, so that somebody could keep the
key to lend, so that anybody who borrowed
it could give a little tip when he brought it
back.

Before I go any further I want to explain
one little thing. This Tintagel Head, where
we were now, is a great, dome-like mass of
rock, standing up out of the sea, with just the
narrow, rocky ridge that I spoke of before to
hold it to the mainland. Everybody at Tintagel calls it "the island," and I call it so sometimes, because that is an easy name for it. But
it is not really an island, and I explain this to
you, because, when you go to Tintagel yourself, I don't want you to say that I deceived
you about it.

We thought that the part of the castle that
we found here was even more interesting than
the part over on the mainland. In some places
the walls had been levelled to the ground, but
we could trace their foundations and see where
rooms had been. Tiny rooms they must have
been, too, some of them. Then we found what

seemed to have been a court-yard. There was
a beautiful bit of old wall at one side of it, with
ramparts like a flight of stairs. On another
side the wall was the natural rock of the island.
Far down below us, close to the edge of the
water, there was another wall, with a door in
it. We felt sure that this must have been
where Tristram and Isolt landed, when they
came from Ireland. We did not dare to go
down to it. The hill was so steep that we were
afraid that if we once started down it we could
not stop, and then we might miss our aim and
go into the water, instead of against the wall.

So we climbed up, instead of down, and
strolled about the island. A little way from
the castle we found a place like a long, narrow
room, with a wall around it. The wall was no
higher than the ground outside, but inside the
ground was a little lower. There was a door
at one end, and at the other end there was a
flat stone, raised up like a table. This room
was the chapel of the castle, and the flat stone
was the altar. We stood before it and tried to
think how it looked here on that day when
King Uther Pendragon and Ygerne stood before this altar and were married. Here stood
Uther, a true king of those rough old days, not
a bit the less happy because he had killed this
woman's husband only a few days before.
Here stood Ygerne, thinking more about the

Duke who had been her husband than about
the King who was to be, letting herself be married to him, just because her friends thought
that they should all be safer so, yet not seeing
anything so very strange in it all, because she
belonged to those same rough old days too.
And there were the King's men, glad of it all because it made the King happy, and the Duke's
men, ready, now that he was dead, to be just as
true to the King as they had ever been to the
Duke.

We found the graveyard of the castle, too,
and the place that they call King Arthur's Seat.
It is like a double throne, strangely hollowed
out of the rock, looking toward the land. It was
not a comfortable place to sit, and we found
a much better one on the other side of the
island. There we sat in the grass and looked
out over the bright sea, down toward the
Land's End and Lyonnesse again, and across to
the west, over the way that Tristram and
Isolt had sailed here together. And we sat so
still that the sheep came and fed near us, and
the sea-gulls circled about, with their queer,
sharp little cries, and shot past us so close, sometimes, that it seemed as if we could almost
reach out and touch them.

"Once upon a time," I said, "Lancelot rode
through the street of the village where we
walked a little while ago. As he passed, the

people called to him and told him to turn back and go no nearer to the castle. If he went there, they said, he would surely be killed by the two giants who lived there.

"I don't know how the castle happened to belong to these giants. Long ago it belonged to Gorlois, the Duke of Cornwall, and after that to Uther Pendragon. Then King Mark had it, and I can't quite make out when these giants got it or how. But you see that there are so many of these different stories that when two of them are brought together they sometimes disagree as badly as the knights usually did when they were brought together.

"Of course you know, without being told, that Lancelot was not very likely to turn back just because somebody told him that he would get killed if he went on. The men who got on well in those days were the ones who dashed straight at things and went through them, without thinking anything about getting killed or not getting killed.

"So Lancelot rode on to the castle, and in at the little arched gateway, over there on the mainland. Then, as soon as he had passed it, the gate fell behind him, and he could not have gone back if he would. But he did not care about going back. When Lancelot had any fighting to do, what he wanted was a good place to fight, not a good place to run away.

He thought that the court of the castle looked like a good place, and he had no more than made up his mind to that when he saw the giants coming.

"Have you ever noticed, when people kill giants in stories, what quick work they generally make of it? I suppose it has to be that way. If the giant got a chance to strike one or two fair blows at his enemy, no doubt that would be the end of the fight and the giant would not get killed at all. And giants seem to depend on that, for you must have noticed, too, that they seldom fight like other men, and they seldom use any weapon but a club. Giants are a stupid lot, and if they cannot crush their enemies all at once they are done for. Perhaps I might worry some sort of moral out of that, but I won't bother you with it.

"So one of these two giants came upon Lancelot and aimed a blow at him with his club. Lancelot caught it on his shield and then struck the giant on the head with his sword and killed him. When the other giant saw that he ran away. Of course he could not run far, and he must have wished that they had not been in such a hurry about dropping the gate so that Lancelot could not get out. As it was, they were both shut in, and there was nothing for Lancelot to do but to run after the giant and kill him. And that he did.

" Then he went into the hall of the castle, and there he found sixty gentlewomen. They told him that the giants had kept them prisoners there and had made them work for them. Some of them had been there for seven years, and often knights had come and had tried to kill the giants and to set them free, but the giants had killed them all. Lancelot told them that they were all free now, and that they could take all the treasure that the giants had piled up and divide it among themselves. Of course there is really no need of my telling you that, because that was what people who killed giants that had castles always did.

" Then Lancelot left Tintagel and rode for many days through the woods and over hills and valleys and across rivers. And one night he came to a house where an old woman lived, and he asked her to let him stay till morning. She was glad to have him stay, and when it was time to go to bed she took him to a room above the gate. There Lancelot laid his armor beside his bed and went to sleep. But he had not slept long when he was awakened by a great knocking at the gate.

" Lancelot jumped out of bed and went to the window, and there, just below him, he saw a knight knocking with the hilt of his sword, and not far off came three other knights, riding toward him. Then the three knights attacked

the one who was at the gate with their swords,
all at once, while he set his back against the
wall and fought with them the best he could.

"Now this was not at all Lancelot's notion
of a fair fight, so he quickly put on his armor,
took a sheet from the bed, fastened it at the
window, and let himself down by it outside. Then he called to the three knights to
leave the one knight and come and fight with
him. So instantly they all turned upon Lancelot, for they seemed to have no notion of
fighting with less than three men to one. But
fighting with Lancelot was a very different
matter from fighting with the other knight.
He was more than a match for all of them, and
when the other knight tried to help him Lancelot told him to keep away and let him fight
alone. And the other knight, seeing that Lancelot was doing very well without him, kept
away.

"Of course they were not very good fighters,
or they would fight a single enemy one at a
time, like good knights, and so it was not long
before Lancelot had them all down on the
ground and at his mercy. They all begged
him not to kill them and said that they would
give themselves up to him and do whatever he
told them. Lancelot had time now to look at
the knight whom he had helped, and he saw by
his armor and his shield that he was Sir Kay.

'You shall not give yourselves up to me,' said Lancelot, 'but to Sir Kay. Yield to him or i will not spare your lives.'

"'We cannot yield to him,' they said, 'for we should have beaten him but for you. We will give ourselves to you, but not to him.'

"'Yield to Sir Kay,' said Lancelot again, 'or I shall not let you live.'

"So the three knights saw that there was nothing to do but just what Lancelot said, and they answered that rather than die they would yield to Sir Kay. Then Lancelot commanded them to go to the court of King Arthur and say to Queen Guinevere that Sir Kay had sent them to be her prisoners.

"The knights rode way and Lancelot and Kay knocked again at the door till the old woman came and opened it for them. She was surprised enough to see Lancelot there, because she had left him only a little while before in his room and the door had not been opened since. She led Lancelot back to the room over the gate, and Kay with him, and there they both went to sleep. In the morning Lancelot was awake before Kay. He got up, dressed himself in Kay's armor, took Kay's shield, found his horse, and rode away, without saying a word to anybody.

"Then Kay awoke and found that Lancelot was gone, and that his own armor and shield were gone, too, but there were Lancelot's lying beside the bed. 'I see why he has done this,' said Kay to himself. 'He is fonder of fighting than I am, and when other knights see him in my armor they will think that it is I and they will all want to fight with him, and he will beat them. And it will be all the better for me too, for when they see me wearing his armor they will think that I am Lancelot, and they will let me alone, so that I can go safely wherever I please.'

"It was just as Kay thought. Every knight whom Lancelot met thought that he was Kay and wanted to fight with him. And Lancelot beat every one of them and ordered them to go to the court of King Arthur and tell Queen Guinevere that Sir Kay had sent them to be her prisoners. And when one knight after another kept coming to the court and saying that Sir Kay had beaten him and sent him there, the King and the Queen and everybody else began to think that Kay must be a better fighter than they had ever believed that he was. And all the time the real Kay was riding about and never having to fight at all, and everybody was getting out of his way, because everybody thought that he was Lancelot.

"And when Lancelot had ridden for many days and was far away from the court, one day in the woods he met a dog, which leaped about

him and then ran away, and came back and
ran around him again and then away, as if it
wanted Lancelot to follow it. So Lancelot followed, and the dog led the way through the
dark wood and across a boggy plain till they
came to a house. The house was old. The
stones of it were covered with moss and some
of them had fallen away, and the broken pieces
of them, covered with moss, too, lay around
the walls. There was a moat and there was a
bridge across it. The bridge was old, too, and
as Lancelot crossed it he heard it crack under
his horse's feet.

"He left his horse and went into the hall,
and there, in the middle of it, he saw a knight
lying dead. Then a woman came and said to
him : 'Oh, knight, you have done me great
wrong, for you have killed my husband!'

"'Is this your husband who lies here?' said
Lancelot. 'I did not kill him, and I am sorry
that you have lost him.'

"'Not you then, perhaps,' the woman answered, 'but it was a knight of your Round
Table.'

"'If it was any knight of the Round Table
who killed your husband,' Lancelot said, 'I am
sure that it was in a fair fight. I am sorry for
you, but any knight may chance to be killed so.
What was your husband's name?'

"'He was Sir Gilbert,' she said, 'and one of

the best knights in the world, and I do not know the name of the knight who killed him.'

"Then Lancelot rode away, across the old, shaking bridge again, across the wide bog and into the forest. And there he met a girl who said to him : ' Come, Sir Knight, and help my brother, who is in a castle near here, wounded.'

" ' Who is your brother,' Lancelot asked, ' and how shall I help him ? '

" ' He is a knight of the Round Table,' she said. ' He fought with Sir Gilbert to-day a fair battle and killed him ; but my brother was wounded too, so that he will die if he does not have help. There is a woman near here who knows magic, and she says that his wounds cannot be cured unless they are touched with Sir Gilbert's sword and with a piece of the bloody cloth that Sir Gilbert is wrapped in. They are in the Chapel Perilous, where Sir Gilbert's body lies, and my brother will die soon unless some knight can go there and bring them to him.'

" ' I will bring them,' said Lancelot ; ' where is the Chapel Perilous ? '

" She pointed the way and said : ' Bring them quickly, Sir Knight, and meet me here, or my brother will die.'

"So Lancelot rode away and came soon to the Chapel Perilous. It stood in a yard with a wall around it. Lancelot left his horse at the

gate and went into the yard, and there, before
the door of the chapel, were thirty knights.
They were all giants, half as tall again as common men. The visors of their helmets were
open and Lancelot could see their faces. They
were hard, pale faces, with deep-sunken black
eyes and cruel mouths. Their armor was all
black, and they all had great black shields, and
drawn swords in their hands.

"Lancelot put his own shield before him and
drew his sword, and went straight toward the
door of the chapel. The giant knights rushed
toward him and struck at him with their swords,
but when he was close to them they all fell back
to right and left and let him pass, and not one
of their swords touched him. They were en-
chanted knights and they could harm only a
man who was afraid of them. You may find,
sometime, when troubles or dangers seem to be
all around you, that the best thing to do is to
throw your shield before you and take your
sword in your hand, and walk through them
and fear nothing.

"So Lancelot came into the chapel. There
was no light except from one little lamp, and
when his eyes had grown used to the darkness
he saw Sir Gilbert lying just as he had left him
lying in the old house. He could not guess
how he had come here, but everything here
seemed to be enchantment, and Lancelot felt

that he scarcely knew whether there had ever been any Sir Gilbert really, or whether he was some ghost or strange fairy, or perhaps nothing at all but a part of the magic of the place. But he went to the dead knight and cut off a piece of the cloth that he was wrapped in, and as he did it the earth shook under him. Then he took the sword that lay beside the dead knight and went out of the chapel.

" And as he came out all the giant knights called to him : ' Sir Lancelot, Sir Lancelot, put down that sword or you shall die ! '

" And Lancelot answered : ' Take the sword from me if you can ; I shall not give it to you for asking.' And he walked safely among them, as he had done before, and mounted his horse and rode back to find the girl.

" And the girl cried with joy when she saw him, and she led him quickly to the castle where her brother was. The wounded knight was so weak that he could scarcely speak, and he was pale from the blood that he had lost, but as soon as Lancelot saw him he knew him— a good knight whom he had seen often in King Arthur's court. The knight knew him, too. ' Sir Lancelot,' he said, ' can you help me ? I feel that I cannot live much longer.'

" Then Lancelot touched the knight's wounds with Sir Gilbert's sword and with the cloth, and in an instant they were all healed. The color of his face and his strength came back, too, and he rose from where he had been lying and thanked Lancelot for saving his life. 'To-night,' said Lancelot, 'I will stay here with you ; to-morrow I must go farther on my way; but you go with your sister to the court and tell the King and the Queen that I shall see them and you there soon.'"

CHAPTER XII

THE CHIME OF THE SEA

THE next day was Sunday. After breakfast we found that we had time to take a little
stroll before going to church. We always felt
tempted to go toward the castle, and so we
did this time. But we did not go into it.
When we came near the shore we found that
the tide was out and we thought that it would
be worth while to explore the shore itself a
little.

We went down among the broken rocks in
the little bay on one side of the neck between
the mainland and the island, and we found nothing there to interest us very much. Still, rocks
and waves are never dull, and it was something
to look up at the towering height above us and
see how the masses of slate must have fallen
away from it sometime long ago, carrying a
part of the castle with them. The giants, if
they were giants, who built the castle of Tinta-

gel, built it so that it was safe from men. They made it of the same stone that it stood upon, and they made it so big and strong, and they chose its place so well, that no army of their days could ever take it. Yet all around it were the water and the wind, and they could do what the men could not. The men had not time to take Tintagel, for they must rest and sleep and die. But the water and the wind never died, and they seldom slept or rested. Time was nothing to them. The castle grew old, and still they were as young as they were at first. It was nothing to them that the castle was built of the same rock that it stood upon. The water beat and dashed against the rock itself, and the wind caught the water and hurled it as high as the castle towers. Year after year they wore them away by little and little, and then all at once a great mass of the rock and the castle would fall with a crash that must have echoed for miles along the shore. And so at last they have left them as we see them now. No, not left them, for the wind and the water are working at them still, and the time will come when there will not be so much as a heap of dust to show where this grand old castle stood. Do they call the rocks and the hills eternal? There is nothing eternal on earth but the sea and the wind.

We clambered back over the rocky isthmus,

and went down upon the little beach on the other side, and into the big cave that is there. This cave is a tunnel that goes clear through Tintagel head, right under the castle. It is one of the wonderful things that the wind and the waves have done all along this coast. The great winter storms come driving across the Atlantic and strike with all their force against Cornwall. If Cornwall had not this wall of rock it would all go down under the water as Lyonnesse did. As it is, the constant beating and dashing of the waves and the showering of the spray carve the rocks into all sorts of strange and fine and fantastic shapes, pillars and points and domes and cracks and hollows and caves. We went into this one till we came to a lake that spread clear across it, and then, as we were not prepared to wade, we turned back and found that it was time to go to church.

The Tintagel church is worth seeing, too. It is high up on a bluff, where it looks far out over the sea and over the land. It is built as strong as a castle and it has lasted better, for it is a thousand years old. They have kept it in repair, no doubt, but there is another reason why it has stood firm while the castle has been wasted and worn away. That reason is that they did not try so hard to make it safe. They thought that enemies would come against their

castle, and so, to defend it more easily, they
perched it on the very edges of that deep,
steep chasm. But they feared no enemies for
their church, so they put it where the waves
and the wind did not harm it, all the time that
they were slowly grinding the castle to dust.
Yet they built it to last, for, though it is not
large, it has walls like a fortress and windows
that are only slits in the walls outside and
widen to the size of common windows inside.
They look as if they were made to shoot arrows
through, but they are built so only to give light
without any loss of strength.

> " Firm was their faith, the ancient bands,
> The wise of heart in wood and stone,
> Who reared with stern and trusty hands
> These dark gray towers of days unknown."

A priest who lived a sweet, simple, noble life
a few miles away on this coast, wrote these
lines about his own church, but they are just as
true of the church of Tintagel.

After church and after dinner we set out for
a real walk. We were going to Boscastle, five
miles up the shore. Everybody said that if we
were going to Boscastle we must walk there,
or we should lose all the beauty of the scenery
along the coast. It was not easy walking, for
the shore of Cornwall is shaped like the edge
of a saw, turned up. We were seldom on level

ground, but always going down a hill and then up another hill, so that we could go down again on the other side, and so on for mile after mile. And once we came to a wonderful, wide, deep gorge, with a little brook running along the bottom of it and all its sides covered with tall ferns. There were high rocks, too, and we had to get into the shelter of one of them while a little shower passed over us. The place, as we found out afterward, is called the Valley of Rocks.

But I am not going to try to tell you much about that walk. It takes a better writer than I am to tell about scenery so as to do any good to anybody who has not seen it. There were the spires and the towers and the arches of the rocks, and there were the soft, fresh green and brown of the fields, after the little rain, and again the bright blue and yellow and scarlet of the flowers, and the shining blue and gray of the sea. There were the pure, sweet air, and the strong, free breeze, and it was all very grand and very lovely.

Hundreds of sea-gulls flew around us, and whirled, screaming, past us, and thousands of sea-gulls whitened the rocks where they lived. And now and then some ravens would flutter above our heads for a moment and then sail away again. "Look well at the ravens," I said, "for you may be looking at King Arthur."

Instead of looking at the ravens Helen looked at me. "You know the guard on the coach told us," I said, "that King Arthur was killed in battle at Slaughter Bridge, and you know I told you that I did not know whether he was killed or not. One of the old stories, as you know, says that he and his knights are sleeping down under the ground at Caerleon, and that they will come back sometime to save England when she needs them most. Then there is the one that says that he is waiting for his time in the happy valley of Avalon. But another story says that instead of dying at last King Arthur was changed into a raven, and that he still lives and flies around this Cornish coast. And just because of this it used to be said that no Cornishman and no Englishman would ever kill a raven, for fear that he might kill King Arthur.

"Some people would call that a superstition, no doubt, but if it is, then it is a very good and pretty and harmless one. And could you believe it, if I told you that these same people once believed one of the wickedest and cruelest of superstitions—one that often made them act like cowards and almost thieves? It was not so very long ago, either.

"Look out on that ocean. See how high the waves are. Hear them dashing and breaking down there at the foot of the cliffs.

See how they throw their spray over the broken rocks. And see how jagged and sharp and rough the rocks themselves are. Feel how strong this breeze is, that blows in from the sea. And yet this is a warm, calm, bright summer day. Now try to think of a cold, rough day in winter, with a great storm blowing in from the sea. Think of the waves a dozen times as high. Think of them thundering on the cliffs and hurling their foam high above them and over them. Think of them pounding and crashing on these jagged, broken rocks with a power that we cannot compare with any other in the world. Think of the wind rushing over this place where we are so that we could not stand against it for a moment. Can you imagine what it would all be like? I am afraid neither of us can.

" But I do know that for the ships that pass this is one of the most terrible coasts in the world. Every winter there are wrecks, and sometimes there are many of them. A ship strikes among these rocks, she never can get off again, and in a little while—only a few hours, perhaps—she is ground to pieces. Unless the men on board get help from the shore they may all be drowned and some of them are almost sure to be. And yet, only a few generations ago, the people of this shore used to stand on these rocks and watch ships while they went to pieces, and men while they drowned, and never lift a hand to help them. And why, do you suppose? Because of a belief among them that a stranger saved from the sea would sometime do an injury to those who had saved him. It is all changed now, and the men of Cornwall try to save shipwrecked sailors, and do save them, as if they were their own brothers, and there are no braver or hardier men in the world than they. But there are men living near here to-day, I have no doubt, who can remember when a ship was wrecked only a few miles up this coast and a rocket was fired over her, and a line secured, and every one on board might have been saved, when someone on the shore cut the line and only one man from the ship was saved.

"Some say that this cruel belief was kept alive because so many of the people made a great part of their living by picking up things that were washed ashore from the cargoes of wrecked ships, and they did not want the men to be kept alive to claim the goods. This may be partly true; but, horrible and wicked as the superstition was, I think that they really believed it. And I think this and I think the more kindly of them, because of that other superstition that they must not kill a raven lest they should kill King Arthur. They could not have been wholly cruel at heart."

There is not much that I need to tell you about Boscastle. It is a queer-looking little place, and pretty, too—a few houses in a cluster, struck down into a crack between two cliffs, with a crooked little harbor. The best thing about it is the walk to it from Tintagel. But when we had walked through the village and left it behind us, and came to the church up on the higher ground of the road back to Tintagel, I did think of something that I wanted to say.

"I don't know," I began, "whether this church is quite as old as the one at Tintagel, where we were this morning, or not. I fancy it is not, but it is pretty old. And there is an old story about the two churches. You don't happen to know, I suppose, that the church at Tintagel has five bells in its tower. A peal of bells, they are called, and they are said to be very fine and sweet in tone. I can't say positively, because I have not heard them ring yet. But the bells were there a long time ago, and the Tintagel people were very proud of them, and they learned to love them, as people do learn to love bells more than almost anything else that is not alive. They called them to church every Sunday; when they were married, they rang for them and seemed to be as glad and happy as anybody. When any of them had been away at sea they heard the bells ring sometimes, as they came toward the shore, and the music made them feel, more than anything else, that they were near home again. When they died, the bells tolled for them. And when they heard the bells tolling for others, the thought might come to them that even if all their other friends should go before, yet, when their own time came, the bells would still be as strong and sound as ever and would be sorry that they were gone.

" But in the tower of the church here at Boscastle there were no bells. Sometimes, when the wind was the right way and the sea was not too loud, they could hear the bells of Tintagel, and then their own tower seemed all the more silent and dull. So at last the people of Boscastle resolved that they would have some bells as good as those of Tintagel. They got some money together and sent it to London to have the bells made. The bells were made and put on board a ship to be brought to Boscastle. The ship sailed down the Thames and down the Channel and around the Land's End and so up the coast.

" The Tintagel bells were ringing as the ship passed, and the men on board could hear them. The pilot was a Tintagel man and the bells told him that he was near home. They made him think of his wife and his children, waiting for him up there in the little village on the hill, and he said : ' Thank God, we are near the harbor and shall soon be safe in and with our friends again.'

" The captain of the ship heard him and he said : ' It will be time enough to thank God when we get on shore ; while we are at sea thank the good ship and the captain that rules her, and your own skill that steers her.'

" ' No, no,' the pilot answered ; ' we must thank God always ; whatever we do ourselves is by His help.'

" ' When you are on my ship,' said the captain, ' thank me ; that is enough.'

" And just as the captain had said it, out of the clear sky a great wind struck the ship and she heeled over, and the water rushed over her deck and she filled. There was a cry of the men for help and one fierce jangle of the bells, and the ship went down. The captain was drowned, but the pilot was saved, and whether the other men were drowned or saved I do not know.

" And so the bells were never brought to Boscastle, and for many years the tower here was silent. Some one tells me that it has one little bell now, but it has no peal like the one at Tintagel. But they say that sometimes, when the waves are high and the storm-wind is blowing as it blew when that ship went down, the gale that comes in from the ocean brings a sound of bells. And then the people of Boscastle listen and say: 'Our bells are ringing down under the water as they ought to have rung all these years in our silent tower.' "

CHAPTER XIII

HOW THE SCABBARD WAS LOST

WHEN we had seen Boscastle we thought that
we had had enough of climbing up hills and
scrambling down on the other side, so we found
a carriage to take us back to Tintagel. The
road was back some way from the shore, and
so it was reasonably smooth and even and level
for the most of the way. As we passed near
the Valley of Rocks we saw a sign-board beside
the road. It said that if we wanted to see St.
Neighton's Kieve we must come in here and
go up to the other end of the meadow to a
house where the key was kept. Some one had
told us that we really ought to see St. Neighton's Kieve, so the next day we decided to go
and borrow the key and see it.

An old man with a long white beard and
shaggy white eyebrows lived in the house
where the key was kept. He asked us to sit
down and rest a little while before we went to

see St. Neighton's Kieve, and he showed us
some queer old carved furniture that he had.
This old man's eyebrows reminded me of
Yspaddaden Penkawr's, that fell down over his
eyes so that he could not see, for this man did
not look as if he saw us at all. He sat before
us and close to us, but his eyes seemed to be
looking down at the floor all the time, and he
talked in a voice that sounded as if it came
from the next room. We tried to get him to
tell us some of the stories of the place, but he
seemed to know nothing about them. He did
not want to talk about Tintagel, or Boscastle,
or St. Neighton's Kieve. He wanted to talk
about America. He had a paper with pictures
of some buildings in America and he asked us
if they were really as beautiful as they looked
in the pictures. We told him that they were
much more so—that he could not think how
beautiful they were unless he saw them. That
was really true, but he found it hard to believe.
He thought that America must be a wonderful
country, and we thought so too.

Then he gave us the key and a printed card
to tell us how to go, and we set out to discover
St. Neighton's Kieve. The path led us into the
Valley of Rocks and up the course of the little
brook that ran at the bottom of it. It was only
a little way, but one of the prettiest walks we
had ever seen. We felt grateful to the stranger

who had been kind enough to tell us we must come here. We crossed the brook twice, went up a little hill and came to a fence with a locked door. This was where we needed the key. We went through the gate and down the hill to the brook again, and looked up at a waterfall that came down in two leaps from high above our heads and fell into a round basin at our feet. I don't know much about St. Neighton, but kieve is an old Cornish word that means tub, so this was St. Neighton's Tub.

When we had stood and looked at it for a long time we turned away and went up the hill again, locked the gate after us, and took our way back through the Valley of Rocks. And now we looked more at the valley than we had done before. It was a strangely beautiful place. Sometimes as we looked down the valley we could see nothing but ferns on either side, or perhaps just here and there a tree— steep, high banks on banks of ferns, and nothing else in sight. The ferns that grew near us were often as high as our heads, and sometimes we could even stand under them, while they bent the tips of their leaves above us like trees. Then, as we walked farther along, we could see where there were great rocks, high up on the side of the valley, yet even these were covered with green vines, so that not a bit of the rock itself could be seen. It was as if there had been some law in the making of the valley that there must be nothing in it to look hard or rough.

" I have never seen a place," I said, " except the valley of our own Hudson, that looked so much like a home for fairies. I should almost think that King Arthur's sister, Queen Morgan-le-Fay, might have lived here. I wonder if it was not here that she came to learn that magic which she knew so well. It would seem strange that any one should learn such wicked magic as hers in such a beautiful place as this. But I think she must have been wicked in the first place, so that any magic or anything else that she could learn was bound to turn out evil. I don't know why she did such dreadful things, or why she hated her brother, King Arthur, so. I suppose it was just because he was good and she was bad."

" What dreadful things did she do ? " Helen asked.

" Well, perhaps the very worst thing that she ever did was to try to kill King Arthur and steal his sword Excalibur. You remember Merlin told Arthur that he must guard the scabbard of Excalibur more than anything else that he had, because while he had it about him he could lose no blood, no matter how much he might be wounded. Now I can't think what should put it into Arthur's head that the best way to keep the scabbard safe was to give it to his sister, Morgan-le-Fay, to keep for him. Of course he did not know how wicked she was or how much she hated him. Still I don't know why he should not keep the scabbard himself. Or, if he wanted somebody else to look after it for him, why did he not give it to Queen Guinevere? But he didn't; he gave it to Morgan-le-Fay, and she set about studying how she could get the sword as well, and how she could kill King Arthur.

"There was one of King Arthur's knights named Sir Accolon. He was a good knight and he always meant to do what was right, I suppose. But he was one of those silly fellows with whom a beautiful woman can always do just about what she likes. He saw Queen Morgan-le-Fay, he saw how beautiful she was, and so he took it for granted that everything that she did or said or thought must be right. So she just took hold of him and did what she liked with him. And what she liked was to use him for her own plans, without even letting him know what she was doing or what he was doing himself. If she had let him know what he was doing I don't suppose he would have done it.

"Well, it happened one day that King Arthur and some of his knights were hunting. And King Arthur and this Sir Accolon and

King Urien, the husband of Morgan-le-Fay, followed a hart till they were far away from the other knights. They rode so far and so long that their horses grew tired and could not carry them. Then they got off their horses and went a little way on foot, till they saw the hart, not far before them, lying on the bank of a broad lake. But they saw something else that made them wonder so much that they forgot about the hart.

"Out on the lake there was a boat, all covered with silk canopies and hangings down to the edge of the water. It was coming straight toward them, and soon it touched the land close to where they were. Then Arthur went to the boat and looked in. The whole of it seemed empty, and he called to the others to come and look. The others came, and they all went into the boat and looked around them, wondering how it could have come there all by itself. All about them there were rich and beautiful silk curtains and cushioned seats and heavy, soft carpets, but no people. They had ridden so long in the hunt that evening was coming on now, when all at once the whole of the place where they were was lighted up, as if it had been noon. Rows of torches, that they had not seen before, all along the sides of the boat, blazed up of themselves and burned with soft-colored lights. And a thin smoke came from them and spread about like incense and filled the place with perfume.

"They had scarcely time to wonder at this when there came twelve girls, who knelt before the King and called him by name and welcomed him and begged him to stay in the boat all night. Then they opened the curtains and led the three knights into another part of the boat, where there was a table richly spread with gold and silver dishes and everything that they could want to eat and drink. The twelve girls served them while they ate, and then they led each of them to a chamber, as rich and beautiful as everything else had been, and told them to sleep there till morning. And as soon as each of the three knights was left alone the light of the torches grew dimmer, and the incense smoke from them grew heavier and the smell of it sweeter, and they all slept.

"What became of the boat after that nobody ever knew, except Morgan-le-Fay and the twelve girls who made up the crew. King Urien awoke in the morning and found himself in his own bed at Camelot. But King Arthur had no such good fortune. When he awoke he was lying on stone. It was all dark around him. He felt the stone on which he lay with his hands. It was smooth and it had lines in it, where stones were fitted together. He knew that it was a floor. Then he reached farther with his hands and touched a wall. He turned his face, and up above him and a little way off he saw a square spot of pale light. The spot of light had black bars across it. He knew from that the sort of place that he was in. It was a prison. Then he heard sounds—a groan —a deep, long sigh, and another groan. 'Who are you,' he asked, 'and what is your trouble?'

"There was no answer for a moment, and then a voice not far from him said: 'Who are you that you do not know? We are knights— twenty of us. We have been here for years, some of us. We are the prisoners of Sir Damas, who owns this castle, and you must be his prisoner too.'

"'Why are you kept here,' the King asked, 'and why have I been brought here?'

"'You are here, it is likely,' the voice answered, 'for the same cause as the rest of us. We are kept here because we will not fight for this Sir Damas. He is a coward and does not dare to fight for himself. He has a brother, Sir Onzlake, a good knight, and he keeps his rightful possessions from him. He cannot keep all, for Sir Onzlake is as brave as Sir Damas is cowardly, and he has one good castle that Sir Damas cannot take from him. And many times Sir Onzlake has offered to fight with Sir Damas for all that ought to be his without fighting. And Sir Damas does not dare to try the battle, but he hopes to find some other knight to fight it for him. But all the good knights who know him hate him so that they will not help him, so he and his men watch the roads and take prisoners the knights that pass. Then he tries to make them fight his brother Sir Onzlake for him, and when they refuse he puts them here in this prison. This is how we have all come here, for we will die rather than fight for such a traitor. And some of us have died from hunger and from the cold and damp of the dungeon. This is why you are here too, no doubt. They will send for you by and by, to ask you if you will fight for Sir Damas.'

"Then Arthur thought of what he ought to do. 'If I say that I will not fight for this Sir Damas,' he thought, 'he will keep me and all these poor knights here till we die. If I fight with Onzlake for him and Onzlake kills me, it will be no worse than dying in this prison, and if I beat Onzlake I will not kill him, and then, because I am the King, I can make Sir Damas give his brother all that is rightly his, and I can make him release these knights.'

"Then the little spot of light high up in the wall was darkened, and Arthur looked up there and saw the face of a girl, looking down into the dungeon. 'Knight,' she said, 'you must fight for Sir Damas with his brother Sir Onz-

lake, or you will never come out of this prison.
Will you fight for him?'

" ' Tell Sir Damas,' Arthur answered, 'that I
will fight for him if he will promise me that,
whether I win or lose, all these knights who
are here in this prison shall be freed.'

" The girl went away, and in a little while
men came and led Arthur out of the dungeon
and up into the hall of the castle, where Sir Damas was. And there Arthur promised to fight
the battle for Sir Damas, and Sir Damas promised to free all his prisoners, whether Arthur
should win or lose.

"Now the story goes back to Sir Accolon.
He went to sleep in the boat, just as King
Arthur and King Urien did. When he awoke
he was lying on the ground, in a forest, just on
the edge of a deep well. He was so near it
that he started quickly away when he saw it,
and as he turned, in getting away from the
dangerous place, he saw an ugly dwarf standing and staring at him. In his hand the dwarf
held a sword, in a beautiful scabbard, all covered with jewels. 'Sir Accolon,' said the
dwarf, 'I am sent to you by Queen Morgan-le-
Fay. She bade me tell you that to-morrow you
should fight with a knight. But you are to
have no fear of him, good knight though he is,
for she has sent you here King Arthur's sword,
Excalibur, to fight him with.'

" 'And where am I to find the knight?' Sir Accolon asked.

" 'Have no fear about that,' the dwarf answered; 'you will find him when the time comes.'

" Then Sir Accolon thought that he understood the whole plan, but he did not; he understood only a little of it. 'Was the boat where we slept,' he asked, 'all an enchantment of Queen Morgan-le-Fay's to get me here and to get me King Arthur's sword to fight with?'

" 'Yes,' said the dwarf.

" 'Then,' said Accolon, 'give my thanks to Queen Morgan-le-Fay and tell her that I will fight the battle for her.'

" The dwarf gave Sir Accolon the sword and left him wondering how he was to know what knight he was to fight and how he was to find him. Soon a knight, with six squires, came riding past, and when he saw Accolon he asked him to come with him to his castle, which was near. And Accolon, since he did not know at all where he ought to go, thought that it would be best to go wherever chance should lead him; so he went with the knight. And who should this knight be but Sir Onzlake, and they had scarcely reached his castle when a message came from his brother, Sir Damas. It said that Sir Damas had found a knight to fight for him, and that Sir Onzlake must be ready to meet him early the next morning in the field beside his brother's castle.

" 'What shall I do,' said Sir Onzlake, when he had heard this message; 'this is the battle that I have wished for so long, and I was wounded with a spear only a little while ago and I am not strong enough yet to fight.'

" 'I will tell you what you shall do,' said Accolon; 'you shall go to-morrow and see the battle, and I will fight it for you. It was told to me that I should fight with a knight to-morrow, and I have King Arthur's sword, Excalibur, and the scabbard. It is the best sword in the world, and while I have the scabbard about me I can lose no blood, so I shall win the battle for you.'

" So Sir Onzlake sent back word that a good knight would be ready to fight for him, and early the next morning they rode to Sir Damas's castle. They stayed in the field near the castle and sent a squire to say that they were ready and were waiting for his knight. Then Arthur rode out from the castle with arms and a horse that Sir Damas had given him. As he reached the gate a girl on horseback met him and came so close that nobody but himself could hear what she said. And she said to him: 'My lord Arthur, your sister, Queen Morgan-le-Fay, sends you your sword, Excalibur, and its scabbard,' and she gave him a sword and a scabbard

that looked so like his own that he had never a
doubt that they were his. But they were a
poor sword and a worthless scabbard that
Morgan-le-Fay had made by enchantment to
deceive the King.

" Then, as Arthur took his place for the first
charge, he saw the prisoners, who had been
freed from the dungeon, coming out of the castle to see the battle. They were all pale and
thin and worn and hungry-looking. Some
of them—those who had been in the prison
longest—could not walk alone, and they leaned
on the others till they came to a place where
they could see well, and there they all sat down
upon the grass. Then they breathed the pure,
fresh, morning air, and gazed about at the
bright sunlight that was shining over everything. They could scarcely bear the light at
first, but soon they could see better. And then
they looked at the levels and slopes of grass
and the green trees, and up at the bright sky,
with the light, white clouds floating in it, and
back at the walls of the castle that had been
their prison. These were beautiful, too, with
their soft colors and the morning sunshine on
them ; and the prisoners could scarcely believe
that they were really free at last and that now
they were to see such lovely things as these
every day. There was one of them who had
been in that dungeon for many years and yet

was not old. He should have been a strong knight, full of life and vigor, but he was so weak that he could scarcely even sit. And when his fellow-prisoner, on whom he had been leaning, moved away from him, suddenly his head grew dizzy and he fell forward upon the grass, and there, close to his face, he saw a little white and pink star of a daisy. He picked it and touched the little rays and the yellow centre with his fingers, and held it close to his eyes, till drops of water came into them and he could not see it any more. He had been shut in by those black walls so long that he had come almost to believe that there were no such things in the world as blue sky and grass and daisies any more.

" Then there was a sharp, clear note from a herald's trumpet, and at the sound all the prisoners, who had been more like sick children a minute before, were knights again. They looked at the two who were to fight, at their horses and their armor, which were as strange to them as the daylight was. They remembered the fine old battles which they themselves had seen and fought, and they tried to judge which of these two would win. They tried to judge, too, which of them they wanted to see win, for one of these knights had set them free, yet he was fighting for the coward and the traitor and the tyrant who had kept them in prison. And the other knight was fighting for the right. If they had known, as Arthur did, that in this strange battle the right was fighting on both sides and must win, they could have looked on more cheerfully.

" Both the men and both the horses were thrown to the ground at the first charge. Both the knights were on their feet in a moment and had begun the fight with swords, and I suppose there was never a stranger sword-fight than that, for Arthur fought hard and well, and yet there was no strength and no sharpness in his sword. He struck his enemy with it, but it would scarcely cut at all; and if it did give some little wound, the knight seemed not to mind it and he fought as well as before. But wherever Sir Accolon's sword struck, it bit into the very steel of Arthur's armor and cut through it and wounded the flesh; and the blood flowed from the wounds and Arthur felt himself growing weaker, and he touched the scabbard by his side to find if it were still there, and could not understand it.

" And when they had fought so for a long time Arthur felt that he could stand only a little longer. If he were to win the battle he must win it now, and he rushed upon Accolon and struck him a great blow on the helmet, and with that his treacherous sword broke in pieces and left him with only the handle in his hand.

Then Accolon struck at Arthur and wounded him again, and Arthur saw that only one chance was left for him. He put his shield in front of him and rushed with a crash against Accolon and at the same time he struck him, with all the strength that he had left, upon the helmet with the handle of the broken sword. Accolon fell and the sword flew out of his hand. Arthur caught up the sword from the ground and the moment that he had it in his hand he knew that it was his own Excalibur. He sprang upon Accolon again, tore the scabbard from his side and threw it far off in the field. Then he struck Accolon one more blow with the sword and the battle was ended.

" Then Arthur cut the lacings of his enemy's helmet and took it off, and saw that the knight he had been fighting was his own knight, Sir Accolon. 'Accolon,' he said, 'where did you get this sword?'

" ' It is King Arthur's sword,' said Accolon, ' and his sister, Queen Morgan-le-Fay, gave it to me to fight this battle. But you have won in spite of it. Will you tell me who you are?'

" ' Yes, Accolon,' the King answered, ' I am Arthur.'

" ' Oh, my lord, have mercy on me, then,' Accolon cried, ' for I did not know you.'

" ' I believe that you did not,' said Arthur, ' and you shall have mercy.'

" Then Arthur called the two brothers, Sir
Damas and Sir Onzlake. ' Sir Damas,' he said,
' I have fought this battle for you and I have
won it. All the lands and castles and whatever else you and your brother have quarrelled
about are yours. I was your champion and I
have won them for you. But now the battle is
over and I am your champion no longer. I am
the King now. Sir Damas, you are a coward
and a tyrant, and you are not fit to be a knight.
This is what I command you: First you shall
give to each of these knights who have been
your prisoners the arms that he had when he
came here, or others as good, and you shall give
each of them a horse. After that you shall
give everything else that you have to your
brother, Sir Onzlake, and he shall give you
one house to live in and one horse to ride—a
palfrey, not a war-horse. Such a man as you
should never ride a war-horse. And you, Sir
Onzlake—I have heard such good report of
you that you shall come to my court, if you
will, and be one of my knights. And now, Sir
Onzlake, I am wounded and weary. Tell me
how far I am from Camelot.'

" ' It is two days' journey, my lord,' said Sir
Onzlake; ' but only a little way from here there
is an abbey where you can rest as long as you
wish and have what care you need.'

" So Arthur went with Sir Onzlake to the

abbey, and the nuns took care of him, and he stayed there while his wounds were healing.

"Now when Morgan-le-Fay heard that King Arthur had not been killed, and that he had his sword Excalibur and the scabbard, she began to think how she should get them again. And she was never slow at thinking. When she had thought, she took forty of her own knights and left Camelot and rode with them to the abbey where King Arthur was. 'Is King Arthur here?' she asked of the nuns.

"'Yes,' they answered, 'he is here.'

"'Take me to him, then.'

"'He is asleep now,' they answered; 'you cannot see him till he wakes.'

"'I must see him now,' she said; 'I am his sister, Queen Morgan-le-Fay.'

"When they heard that they did not dare to disobey her, so they led her to the room where the King was. He was sleeping, but his sword Excalibur was in his hand and the scabbard lay a little way off. It was the sword that Morgan-le-Fay wanted, but she did not dare to take it, for fear of waking the King, so she took the scabbard, left the abbey quickly, mounted her horse, and rode away with her knights.

"She was scarcely gone when the King awoke and missed the scabbard. He called some of the nuns and asked who had taken it, and they told him that it was his sister and that they had not dared to disobey her commands. And surely, when Arthur himself had trusted his sister so long, he could not blame the poor nuns for trusting her. His wounds were nearly well by this time, so he sent for his horse and began to put on his armor, and he sent for Sir Onzlake and told him to put on his armor and be ready to ride with him.

" As soon as they were both ready they rode the way that Morgan-le-Fay and her knights had gone, and in a little while they saw them far ahead. As fast as they could King Arthur and Sir Onzlake followed, and the forty knights of Morgan-le-Fay were such good, brave knights that they thought of nothing but of getting away from the two who were coming after them. So they all rode on through a forest and then out upon a plain, and all the time King Arthur and Sir Onzlake were gaining. And Morgan-le-Fay was passing near a little lake when she looked back and saw that her brother would soon overtake her. She could not hope to keep the scabbard of Excalibur, but, rather than let him have it, she threw it as far as she could out into the lake. It whirled through the air in an arch, and its jewels made a rainbow in the sunlight, and then it sank into the water and nobody ever saw it again.

" But still King Arthur and Sir Onzlake fol-

lowed Morgan-le-Fay and her knights, and still
they gained on them. At last the Queen and
the knights rode down into a valley, and the
King and his knight were out of sight over
the brow of the hill. But the Queen knew
that before her company could climb the hill
on the other side her brother would come up
with them. Then, in an instant, by the magic
that she knew how to use, she changed herself
and all her knights and their horses into stone.
In a moment King Arthur and Sir Onzlake
were among them, and they looked about and
there was a statue of a queen on a horse and
there were statues of forty knights on horses.
' See,' said Arthur, ' God has turned them all
into stone for their wickedness. There is
nothing for us to do.'

" And the King and the knight turned their
horses and rode back toward the abbey. Then,
when they were out of sight, the Queen turned
herself and her knights back to flesh again, and
the whole forty-one of them thanked their stars
that they were safe from the two who had
been following them.

" And so the scabbard of Excalibur was lost
forever. But I don't think that King Arthur
really cared very much. He always trusted to
his own strength and bravery more than to
magic when he was in a fight. He still had the
best sword in the whole world. He could get

another scabbard good enough to carry it in, and a good sword, he thought, was better to guard himself with than any scabbard."

" If Morgan-le-Fay wanted to kill King Arthur," said Helen, " why didn't she kill him when she had him in the boat? "

" I don't know," I said, " why she didn't. People in stories, you know, always do things the longest and the hardest ways. I suppose they do so just to make the stories."

CHAPTER XIV

KING ARTHUR'S GRAVESTONE

THERE are some half-dozen places scattered over the world that I always remember as places of friendliness and rest and happiness. I come back to them, if I am lucky enough to see them for a second time, with a feeling of getting home. I shall feel so, I am sure, if I ever go again to Tintagel, though it was only a little while that we were there.

We left it early in the morning, wishing to have time to see a little of Camelford and Slaughter Bridge and King Arthur's Grave, as they called it, before taking our train.

We rode back along the way that we had come, between those high, slate castle walls, and past the dangerous, deep, harmless-looking pools of water, and among the fields, with their low slate walls and the yellow and scarlet flowers growing on them, and so we came to the Camelford railway station. We found a safe place to leave our luggage and asked the porter to show us the way to Slaughter Bridge. It was only across the track and down the bank and a little way along the muddy road, and we were there. It was just a little stone bridge across a bit of a river, the Camel. Of course we had to stand on it and look up and down the river and all around, and try to think of the place full of fighting men and charging horses. We tried to bring back the picture of the battle, the rushing together of the lines of knights, the shock of their meeting, the clatter of the armor, the men and the horses falling and rolling down and choking up this little stream—yet I had to declare once more that I did not believe that the battle was fought here at all.

Across the river and a little way along the road there was a mill, and there was a blacksmith's shop next to it. The miller, a good-looking young fellow, stood at his door looking at us. We went up to the mill and asked him where King Arthur's gravestone was. Through the gate and just a little up the river and down the bank, he said, we should find it. We tried to go the way he said. We scrambled down the bank and over wet and slippery places and among the bushes, and never a sign of a gravestone could we find. We were quite ashamed of ourselves, because the miller had told us it was so easy to find, but we had to give it up and go back to ask again.

The miller was out of sight when we went back, but the blacksmith was pounding on his anvil and smoking his stump of a pipe and talking to a neighbor who stood by. The blacksmith was an old man, with a thin, straggly, white beard. We told him we could not find King Arthur's gravestone. He began to tell us again, then he stopped and thought for a moment, and then he said: "Shall I go and show you?"

"If you would, please, we should be ever so much obliged."

The old man dropped his hammer, tossed his hot iron back upon the forge, and started briskly off along the road. He turned up the river, plunged down the bank, dashed through the bushes, and then stood still and looked around. King Arthur's gravestone was not where he thought it was, and he did not know where to look for it. We were quite delighted and thought a good deal better of ourselves than we had before. If the blacksmith could not find King Arthur's gravestone, how could we expect to? But the blacksmith knew what he was looking for and we did not, and so in a few minutes he found it.

It was a flat stone, some seven feet long and two wide, lying on the ground. "There are some letters on it," said the old man.

The place was so shady, that, on this dull, cloudy day, it was almost dark. We could scarcely see the letters at all, but we could feel them. We tried to read them, using partly our eyes and partly our fingers, like a blind man. I began: "L-A-T-I-N—and then here are two I's—and then there are some things that don't seem to be any letters that I ever met with before, except now and then an A. L-A-T-I-N spells 'Latin' well enough, but the rest of it doesn't seem to be Latin or anything else."

"A good many 'as tried to read it," said the old man, "but none of 'em can't make nothing out of it."

"There seem to be a good many A's," I said.

The old man grinned. "Maybe they knawed 'ow to make A's best," he said.

After all, we could not think of any better way to account for it, so we accepted that one. "What I can't see," said the blacksmith, "is 'ow they ever got that stone 'ere; it's so 'eavy."

It did not seem strange to me at all. I thought that a yoke of oxen, with a good big chain, could move it easily enough. But of course I did not want to hurt the old man's feelings by saying so.

It is lucky that this is a book of stories and not a book of travels. Because I positively cannot remember which side of the river that stone was on. I do not remember whether we crossed the river on stepping-stones to get back to the blacksmith's shop, or whether we were already on the same side of it. Since this is a book of stories it doesn't matter. I do remember that we went through grass that was so tall and so wet that it did not seem to make much difference whether we were in the river or the grass. We asked the blacksmith the way to Camelford village, he pointed along the road, we gave him our thanks and a little something else, and we set out for a two-mile walk.

"Oh, I don't want this to be Camelot at all," Helen said, as we walked through the street of Camelford.

It was not a pretty place. All the houses were small and poor, and the people looked poor too. The street was not over-clean, and neither were the houses or the people. "I don't want it to be Camelot either," I said, "and even that sign there, 'White Hart—W. Arthur,' shall not convince me that a descendant of King Arthur is keeping an hotel here. We will not even go to Mr. W. Arthur's house for luncheon; we will go to the King's Arms."

The King's Arms seemed to be a very good hotel for such a village as Camelford to have. In the coffee-room there was an account of King Arthur, printed and framed and hung on the wall. I read it while we were waiting for them to bring our luncheon. If it was all true it showed that the great battle was fought somewhere near here, but it showed, too, that King Arthur was not buried at Slaughter Bridge. " But, after all," I said, " how can that stone that we saw be the stone that the story is about unless this is Camelot?"

"Then it really is King Arthur's gravestone?" Helen asked.

"I didn't say it was King Arthur's gravestone; I said 'the stone that the story is about.'"

" Is it another story then?"

"Yes, it is another story, about a very wonderful stone, and I think that the stone that we saw this morning, with the letters on it, must be the very one. But it cannot be unless this Camelford is really Camelot."

"But you said you didn't believe it was Camelot, and you didn't want to believe it."

"Yes, I did say so, but I think we might better believe it, just for the sake of this story."

" But how can we believe it if it isn't so?"

"My child, you must learn my way of believing things whether they are so or not; of believing them when you want to and not believing them when you don't want to. If you can't believe you must make believe.

"Yet the story does not begin here, but at

Caerleon. Once, when King Arthur was holding his court there, a messenger came to him
from King Ryence, of North Wales. He was
the giant, you know, who was making war on
King Leodogran, of Cameliard, that time when
King Arthur went to help him. Well, it seems
that he was beginning to get over the whipping
that he got then, and he was still thinking
about that wonderful mantle that he had, that
was trimmed with kings' beards. So his messenger, who was very polite about it, said that
Arthur must send his beard to Ryence to put
on his mantle, and, as Ryence really wanted it
very much, he should be glad to take it with
him. He said, too, that if Arthur would send it
peaceably and of his own accord King Ryence
would put it in the very best place on his mantle, where it would show much better than any
of the eleven kings' beards that he had already ;
but if Arthur would not send it, then King Ryence would come with an army and take it, and
he would take Arthur's head at the same time.

"'Say to King Ryence,' Arthur answered,
'that I am still so young that my beard is not
long enough to trim a mantle with. Say to
him, too, that, such as it is, if he wants it, he
must come and take it, and, if he does not come
against me soon I shall go against him, to see
which of us shall do homage to the other.'

"Then, as Arthur had a good many other

things to think about, he forgot about Ryence
for a time. And now the story comes here to
Camelot, for it was here that the King was
holding his court when more messengers came
to him to say that Ryence was coming with a
great army, and that Arthur must make ready
to meet him, or all his country would be laid
waste and he himself would be killed. Now
Arthur and his knights were always ready to
meet any enemy who might come, so they did
not feel much frightened.

"And at about the time that the King and all
the knights had heard this news, there came into
the hall a young girl. She went to the King
and threw off her mantle, and showed him that
she wore a big, beautiful sword. 'Why do you
wear that?' the King asked; 'it is strange to
see a girl like you wearing a sword.'

"'My lord,' she answered, 'I cannot take it
off. It has been put on me by enchantment.
And it was told me that nobody could draw
this sword out of its scabbard and free me from
it except the best knight in your court. So I
have come here to see which of your knights
can draw it for me.'

"So King Arthur commanded that every
one of his knights should try to draw the
sword. And they all tried, and they all pulled
hard at the sword, and not one of them could
pull it out of its scabbard. 'You do not need

to try so hard,' the girl said; 'the knight who can draw it at all can draw it easily.'

" I don't know where Lancelot and Gawain and Gareth were. It seems as if one of them ought to have been able to draw the sword. I suppose they were away on some adventures. But there was a poor knight in the hall whose name was Balin. He was not one of Arthur's knights. He had killed one of the King's knights and the King had put him in prison for it, but he had found out that it was in a fair fight and not Balin's fault, and he had let him out, but he had not yet left the court. And as the girl was leaving the hall with her sword Balin asked her to let him try to draw it.

" But the girl looked at his poor clothes and said : 'No; do not trouble me any more; how could you hope to do it when all these good knights have failed.'

" ' Do not judge me so because I am poor,' Balin answered; 'many a good and brave man may wear poor clothes; let me try to draw the sword.'

" So he took hold of the sword and easily drew it out. And he held it up and looked at it, and thought that he had never seen a finer sword. 'Give it back to me now,' said the girl; 'if you keep it, it will bring you bad luck.'

" ' No,' said Balin; 'when a knight has won

a sword in such a way as this, it is his to keep.
I am not afraid of bad luck and I will keep it.'

" ' If you keep it,' said the girl, ' you will always have bad luck; you will do great harm,
and you will kill the man that you love best in
all the world.'

" ' I am not afraid,' said Balin; ' I will keep
the sword.'

" So the girl went out of the hall and away,
and Balin, who meant to leave the court too,
went to King Arthur to take his leave of him.
' Do not go,' said the King, ' and do not be
angry with me because I put you in prison.
I had heard false stories about you and I did
not know what a good knight you were. Stay
with us now and be one of my own knights.'

" ' I thank you, my lord,' Balin answered,
' but I must go now and find adventures and
prove myself the good knight that you say I am.
When I have done that I will come back.'

" So Balin went out of the hall and put on
his armor and rode away. And Merlin said
to the King: ' My lord, there are few better
knights than this Balin, and he will do you
good service, but his own life will be sad and
he will not live long.'

" Balin was not far from Camelot when he
saw a knight coming toward him along the road,
and he knew by the knight's shield and armor
that he was his brother Balan. And when

they met Balan said: 'I heard that you were in prison, and afterward I heard that you were free, and I was coming to Camelot to meet you.'

"And Balin said: 'I am going away from Camelot now. King Arthur was kind to me and begged me to stay, but I want to do some great deed, something to show to King Arthur that I deserve his kindness. You shall go with me and help me now, and we will go against King Ryence. They say he is at Castle Terrabil.'

"So Balan turned and went with Balin. They had not gone far when they met Merlin, but they did not know him, because he was disguised in some way or other. 'Knights,' said Merlin, 'whither are you going?'

"'Who are you,' said Balin, 'that we should tell you?'

"'I will not tell you who I am,' Merlin answered, 'but I will tell you whither you are riding; you are seeking King Ryence, but you will gain nothing by it, unless you have my advice.'

"'I know who you are,' said Balin, 'when you talk like that. You are Merlin, and we will take your advice and thank you for it.'

"Then Merlin led them into a wood and told them to lie down and sleep and he would wake them when it was time. So the two knights lay down and slept till midnight and then Merlin woke them. 'You must be ready now,' he said, 'for King Ryence is coming. He is riding through the wood with some of his knights. Wait here till some of them are past and you see the King himself, and then fall upon him and take him prisoner.'

"It was not long that they had to wait before the company of knights came past. When half of them had gone by Merlin pointed and said: 'There is the King; attack him now and take him!'

"Then Balin and Balan rushed forward and attacked the King and the knights that were next to him. They were all surprised and none of them was ready to fight. In a moment Balin and Balan had wounded half a dozen of them Even very brave men sometimes get frightened at such a time as this, as old soldiers will tell you. In the darkness and the confusion these knights could not see how few men were attacking them. They knew only that some of them were wounded, and they thought that nothing less than a large company would dare to attack them, as many as they were. They did not know whether their enemies were on one side or the other, or all around them, and so they just turned and ran away.

"But the King did not run away. Giant as he was, Balin and Balan had given him two or three wounds before he knew what was going on at all, and now they took good care that he should not get away. When his own knights had left him he was in their hands, and they had only to lead him where they would. They brought him to Camelot, to the gate of the castle of King Arthur, and there they gave him over to the porters and told them to take him before the King. Then they rode away.

"King Ryence was led into the hall, not half so glad to be there as King Arthur was to see him there. King Arthur asked him how he had come there, and Ryence told him all that he knew about the little battle in the wood and the two knights who had taken him prisoner and brought him to Camelot. 'Who were the knights?' King Arthur asked.

"'I do not know,' said Ryence.

"'My lord,' said Merlin, who stood near the King, 'they were Balin, who drew the sword that the girl carried, and his brother Balan.'

"Then Ryence, seeing that there was nothing else to be done, swore to keep peace with King Arthur and to be faithful to him as long as he lived. So the King let him go, and he thought himself very lucky to get away from Camelot alive.

"The story does not tell how Balin and Balan chanced to part, after they had left Camelot again, but the next time that it tells of Balin he was alone. As he rode on his way he came up with a knight and a girl, who were riding together. The knight looked so sorrowful that Balin asked him what it was that made him sad, but the knight would not tell him. 'I would help you if I could,' said Balin.

"'You cannot help me,' said the knight.

"'May I ride with you?' Balin asked.

"'Yes,' said the knight, 'if you wish it.'

"So they rode on together, and they had gone only a little way when, without any warning, a spear struck the knight from behind and he fell down off his horse. 'I am killed,' he cried, 'by a traitor knight named Garlon, who rides invisible. Take my horse, Sir Knight; he is better than yours. Go with this maiden, find this murderer Garlon, and avenge my death,'

"Then the knight died. Balin and the girl rode on, and Balin was very silent and very thoughtful, for, brave man as he was, he was filled with horror at the thought that anyone should have the power to ride without being seen, and to kill men who did not know that anyone was near. He wondered how it could be and how he could find this invisible murderer and punish him. And as they rode on in this way they met another knight. It was Balin who looked sad now, and the other knight asked him why it was. 'A knight was riding with me a little while ago,' said Balin, 'and Garlon, who rides invisible, came behind him

and killed him with a spear.   I am seeking th⸲
Garlon to punish him.'

" ' May I go with you and help you?' said
the other knight.

" ' Yes,' said Balin, ' if you will.'

" But they had scarcely started on again when
another spear came from behind and struck the
knight, and he, too, fell down from his horse
and died.   And Balin and the girl rode on
again, and Balin wondered more and more how
he could ever find and punish this murderer
who could not be seen.   Toward night they
came to a castle and they thought that it would
be best to stay there till morning ; but as Balin
rode in through the gate ahead of the girl, suddenly the portcullis was dropped behind him
and she was left outside.   Then, as he looked
back, he saw that men had surrounded her as
if they would make her a prisoner.   He could
not get back through the gate to help her, so
he ran up to the top of the wall of the castle, at
a place where it was not too high, and jumped
over, and in a moment he was among the men,
with his sword drawn.   But they said to him
' We will not fight with you ; we mean to do
with this maiden only according to the custom
of our castle.'

" That was another of the strange ways that
they had in those days.   Castles had the most
remarkable customs.   Some of them were good

and some of them were wicked and cruel, and some of them were silly. But the people of the castle could do almost anything they liked with strangers, and the strangers would not complain if they only said: 'It is the custom of the castle.'

"'What is the custom of your castle?' Balin asked.

"'The lady of the castle,' the men answered, 'has been sick for a long time. It is said that nothing can ever cure her except the blood of a maiden in a silver dish. So it is the custom of the castle that every maiden who comes this way must give a little of her blood to try whether it will cure our lady. If she will give it of her own accord, it is all the better; if she will not, we make her give it.'

"'If this maiden who is with me,' said Balin, 'wishes to give you some of her blood for your lady, she may give it; if she will not, you shall not harm her.'

"'I will give it gladly,' she said; and so she did, and it did the lady of the castle no good at all.

"They rode on again the next day, and at night they came to another castle, and the lord of it asked them to stay till morning. While they were at supper Balin thought that he heard a groan, as of some one in great pain, and he asked the lord of the castle who it was

'Not long ago,' he answered, 'I was at a tour.
nament, and twice I jousted with another
knight who was there, the brother of King
Pelles, and twice I threw him down. Then, to
be revenged on me, he wounded my son. It is
my son whose groan you heard, for his wound
is not well, and they say that it never can be
made well, except by the blood of the knight
who wounded him. And I cannot find the
knight, because he rides invisible, and I do not
know his name.'

"'I know his name,' said Balin; 'it is Garlon,
and I am seeking him, to punish him for killing two knights who were with me. If I can
find him and kill him, you shall have some of
his blood to heal your son's wound.'

"'Then I will tell you,' the other said, 'how
you can find him. His brother, King Pelles,
will give a great feast at his castle a few days
from now. This Garlon will surely be at the
feast, and there he will not be invisible. Any
knight can come there who brings with him
his wife or his lady. I cannot go, for I have
no wife, but you can go with this maiden who
is with you.'

"'I will go, then,' said Balin, 'for I do not
know how else I can ever find him.'

"So in the morning they set out toward
the castle of King Pelles, and their host went
with them. It was a long way, and when they

came to the King's castle it was already the
first day of the feast. The knight whose son
was wounded could not go into the castle because he had no lady with him, but Balin and
the girl went in. The people of the castle led
Balin to a chamber and took off his armor, and
when it was time for him to go to the table
they asked him to leave his sword in the
chamber, too. But Balin said: 'No, it is the
custom of my country for a knight to wear his
sword always, and I must do so or I must leave
you and your castle and your feast.'

"So they let him wear his sword. Then
they placed him at the table, and the girl who
had come with him sat next to him. Then
Balin said to some one who sat near him: 'Is
there not a knight in this court named Garlon?'

"'Yes,' he answered, 'that is he yonder.'

"Then Balin looked at Garlon and thought:
'He is here among his friends; if I kill him
here they will surely kill me; I cannot es-
cape; yet if I let him go now I may never have
another chance to kill him.'

"Then Garlon saw Balin looking at him, and
he came up to him and struck him in the face
and said: 'Knight, why do you stare at me?
Eat your meat and do what you came for!'

"'I will do what I came for,' said Balin, and
he sprang up and drew his sword and struck
off Garlon's head before anybody could raise

a hand to stop him. Then for an instant he
stood there with his sword in his hand, before
any one could move toward him. He whispered to the girl: 'I have avenged your
knight; take some of the blood of this man
quickly to our host of the castle to cure his
son's wound.'

"Then he set his back against the wall, ready
to guard himself against those who would attack him. And they all started up and came
toward him at once, but King Pelles cried:
'Let nobody touch him but me! I will kill
him myself for killing my brother!'

"So the King caught up a sword and rushed
upon Balin, and aimed a blow at his head.
Balin caught the blow on his own sword, but
his sword broke with the force of it, and fell
in pieces on the floor. Then Balin dashed at
the crowd of knights in front of him, and broke
through it, and ran into another room, and the
King followed him. And Balin went on into
another room, and so on from room to room,
hoping somewhere to find a weapon, and the
King followed close upon him to kill him.

"Then Balin came into a great chamber
that was half-darkened, but he could see that
it was hung all around with rich tapestries and
curtains. And there was a bed, and in the bed
lay an old man, with a long, white beard. He
lay as still as if he were dead, but there was

color in his cheeks and his lips were red. Beside the bed was a table, all of gold and silver,
put together in strange and beautiful patterns.
On the table stood a spear. A little stream of
blood flowed from the point of the spear and
ran down the shaft to the table. And where
the blood touched them the gold and the silver of the table shone brighter than anywhere
else.

"Balin had no time to think of all these
things, but he saw them, and afterward he remembered them. Most of all he saw the spear.
He ran to it and took it in his hand and turned
upon King Pelles, who was close behind him.
As the King came on Balin struck him with
the spear and gave him a deep wound in the
side, and the King fell down as if he were dead.

"But as he struck that stroke Balin felt the
floor tremble under him. It shook so that he
could scarcely stand upon it. He dropped
the spear and it fell with a noise like thunder.
He looked around him and the walls seemed
to be shaking and moving. Then he heard
noises of crashing and splitting, and he felt the
floor going away from under him. A great
burst of light came into the chamber through
the roof, that opened and fell apart. The
thick stone walls tottered and toppled, there
was a mighty roar and crash, as the whole
castle fell into a formless heap, and then

a great cloud of dust rose slowly in the air
and was borne far off by a hot wind that
blew across the pile of ruins where the castle
had stood. Balin felt the downward rush, as
he sank with the floor; he saw the roof split
above him and the walls whirled and tumbled
about him, and he heard the crash of the
shattered stone and timbers, but he did not see
the cloud of dust or feel the hot wind.

"For three days Balin saw and heard and
felt nothing. Then he felt the touch of a hand
and heard a voice say to him softly: 'Balin.'
He opened his eyes and saw a face with a long
beard bending over him. It was Merlin.
'Balin,' said Merlin again, 'it is time for you
to leave this place. I have brought a horse for
you. Get up and come away.'

"Balin was so sore and stiff from lying on
the stones for those three days that he could
scarcely move, but he rose and looked around.
'Do you know,' said Merlin, 'what you have
done?'

"'I know,' said Balin, 'that I killed a murderer. Then King Pelles followed me through
the rooms of the castle, and I know that at last
I found a spear and took it and turned upon
him and wounded him with it. That is all that
I have done. After that the castle all fell down,
but surely I did not do that.'

"'Yes,' Merlin answered, 'you did that and

more than that.   Do you know what this place
is, and who King Pelles is ?   Do you know who
that old man was who lay in the bed in that
chamber where you found the spear ?   That
was Joseph of Arimathæa.   It was he who
buried the Christ after He was crucified.   Long
after that he came into England and brought
with him the Holy Grail, the cup in which he
caught the blood of the Christ when He was on
the cross.   If it had not been for the Holy
Grail Joseph would have been dead hundreds
of years ago.   He is not seen among men any
more, but he still lives, and he will not go out
of the world till the coming of the best knight
of all the world.   The Grail was here in this
castle, and it has kept Joseph alive all these
years.   King Pelles is his descendant and he is
the keeper of the Grail.   And that spear with
which you wounded his side was the very spear
of the Roman soldier who pierced the side of
the Saviour on the cross.'

"'Is he dead, then—King Pelles ?'   Balin
asked.

"'No,' Merlin answered, ' he is not dead, but
he will never be cured of that wound that you
gave him till the best knight of the world
comes.   He will cure him with the blood that
flows from the point of the spear.   It was because you struck him with that spear that the
castle fell ; and because you struck him with

that spear, too, the whole land here is waste
and worthless, and it will be desolate and
worthless till the best knight of all the world
comes and heals the King's wound.'

"Then Balin left Merlin and rode on his way.
And as he passed along he saw that nothing
grew in the fields. If there were flowers they
were old and faded and dead, and they hung
down on their dead stalks. The earth looked
arid and hot, and where there was grass it was
shrivelled and brown and dried, as if the blazing sun of a whole summer had shone on it,
with never any rain or any dew. A hot wind
blew everywhere and caught up the fine, dry
dust and sand, so that they sometimes almost
hid the burning sun and made it look more red
and cruel; and the dust and sand cut against
Balin's face and covered him and his horse till
they were of the color of the dead fields. There
was no water anywhere, and no shade, for the
same hot wind tore the brown, wrinkled leaves
off the trees and mixed them with the dust and
sand. Broken branches of the trees themselves
swayed in the wind, and other trees were split
down their trunks to the roots, or shone with a
ghostly white, where the bark had been torn
off, as if lightning had struck them. Balin saw
few people. Now and then an old man or an
old woman—they all seemed to be old—sat at
the door of a poor, shattered house. None of

them was doing anything, and they all looked
upon the ground with sad, worn, helpless, dull
faces. Yet some of them, as Balin passed,
looked up at him, and a little cold light, like
anger, came into their eyes, as if they knew
that it was he who had made them so wretched.

"You may believe that Balin did not care to
stay in this country, and that he rode through
it and out of it as fast as he could. When he
was away from it he rode more slowly. He
was thinking of all the strange things that he
had seen and done since he left King Arthur's
court. He could not see that he had done any
wrong in killing the murderer Garlon, or in
wounding King Pelles, yet he felt sad because
of all the harm that had come because he
struck that blow with that spear. He could
not understand how that one blow could do so
much harm. Neither can you understand it, I
think, and neither can I.

"You must remember that it was the castle
of the Holy Grail where Balin had been, and
that King Pelles was the keeper of the Holy
Grail. Wherever you find the Holy Grail,
there you will always find wonder and mystery
—things that you do not understand and things
that you will never understand. When we
think and talk and hear of the Holy Grail, it
seems to me always that we see through a mist
and hear from far off. We can see and hear a

great deal, but we can clearly make out only a little.

" So Balin rode on his way puzzled and sad And after a time he met an old man, who said to him: 'Knight, if you ride this way you will come to a castle where you will have trouble and danger. It will be better for you if you turn back.'

" And Balin answered: 'I can have no worse trouble than I have had already, and I do not fear danger. I will go on.'

" So he went on, and soon he came to the castle. And a crowd of ladies came out to meet him and to welcome him, and they led him into the hall and put him at the table, and there were feasting and singing and dancing, and Balin began to wonder what danger it was that he had to fear. Then the lady of the castle said to him: 'Knight, before you go from here you must fight with a knight who keeps an island near by. Every knight must do so who passes this way. It is the custom of the castle.'

" 'It is a bad custom,' said Balin, 'but I will fight with your knight, if I must. If he kills me, I am willing. I have done harm enough and I have had sorrow and trouble enough. I do not care much about my own life. And so, if I am to fight with him, let me go and do it now.'

" Then one of the ladies said: 'Sir Knight

your shield is small, and it looks old and battered. Let me give you a larger and better
one.'

" So Balin took the shield that she brought
him, and they led him to a place where there
was a boat. And he and his horse went into
the boat and were floated over to the island.
And when Balin had landed and was on his
horse he saw coming the knight with whom he
was to fight. They put their spears in rest and
dashed against each other and both of them
were thrown from their horses. Then they
rose and began the battle with swords. It was
a long and a hard battle. Balin had never
fought with so strong a knight as this before.
The fight when he and his brother Balan
caught King Ryence and drove away his men
seemed to him nothing compared with this.
He grew angry that the other knight should
stand against him so long, and he fought as he
had never fought before. The other knight
fought harder too, and each of them had many
wounds.

" At last the knight of the island sank down
upon the ground and said : 'You have beaten
me, Sir Knight. I cannot fight any more, and
I cannot live long with the wounds that you
have given me. I do not care for that. I am
kept here by a cruel custom, and some knight
would kill me in the end. And more than that,

I have lost my brother. I should never see him again, kept here away from the world, and without my brother I do not care to live.'

"Then Balin said: 'Sir Knight, you have killed me, too. Tell me who you are, for I have never fought before with so good a knight.'

"And the other answered: 'I am Balan, the brother of Sir Balin, one of the best knights of the world.'

"And when Balin heard that, being weak with his wounds and with long fighting, he fainted and fell back upon the ground. Then Balan crept up to him and took off his helmet and saw that he was his brother. And when Balin opened his eyes again Balan said to him: 'Why did you carry this strange shield? If you had carried your own shield I should have known you by it.'

"And Balin answered: 'They gave it to me at the castle, because it was better than mine. But tell me why you were here keeping this island in this strange way?'

"'Once,' Balan answered, 'the lady of this castle had a husband, and she would never let him go away from her to any battles or tournaments. And he grew tired of rest and idleness, and so they made this custom—this law—that every knight who passed this way should fight with him. And if ever any knight overcame

him, that knight was to hold the island instead
of him and keep up the custom. At last a
knight killed him and held the island. I killed
the knight who was here when I came, and so I
held the place, and so you would have held it
if you had killed me and saved your own life.'

" Then the lady of the castle came, and Balan
told her that they were brothers and that they
had killed each other, and he asked her to have
them buried there together. Then Balan died,
and Balin died not long after.

" In the morning Merlin came. He found
Balin's sword and took off its hilt and put another hilt on it. The new hilt was rich and
beautiful, with gold and jewels on it, and when
Merlin had put it on the blade he said : ' There
is no sword in the world more wonderful than
this, except King Arthur's sword, Excalibur.
But no knight shall use it now, till the one best
knight of all the world comes to take it.'

" Then Merlin drove the sword into a great
stone, and he wrote on the stone that no knight
should ever draw this sword out of the stone
except the one to whom it should belong, the
best knight of the world. Then he pushed the
stone out into the river and it floated like
wood. And for many years, the story says,
the stone floated on the river, and at last it
drifted down to Camelot.

" Now *if* this is Camelot where we are, *then*

I believe that the stone we saw this morning is that very stone. And if that is the very stone, then the letters on it, that we could not read, are the letters that Merlin put there, which said that no knight but the best knight of all the world should ever draw this sword."

"And what about the sword?" Helen asked.

"The best knight of all the world came and drew it out and carried it away."

"But wasn't Lancelot the best knight in the world, and couldn't he draw the sword?"

"Yes, for a long time Lancelot was the best knight in the world; but the letters on the stone meant that the knight to draw the sword must be the best knight who ever was or ever would be, and Lancelot was not that. It was not till long afterward that a knight came who could draw the sword."

———

When Balin had brought Ryence as a prisoner to Camelot the last of the great enemies of King Arthur stood helpless before him. There was no one left to stand against him now and to say that he should not be King. His lords and his knights and his people all knew him now; yes, and his enemies knew him too. They knew that he had the right to reign over England. They knew that he had the right, first, because he, the new King, was the son of the old King, Uther Pendragon. Better than this, they knew that he had it because God had chosen him when he drew the sword out of the stone at St. Paul's long ago. Best of all, they knew that he was the true King because he ruled faithfully and justly and well. The wrongs that had been before he came were ended, the poor lived and worked in peace, the honest rich man knew that his wealth was safe. If the peasant was true to the King, the King cared for him and guarded him as well as the lord. If the nobleman did wrong he was judged and punished as sternly as the peasant. Arthur's people believed that there had never been before such a great and noble King as theirs, and they were right. In his time no knight was thought to know what true knighthood was till he had been at Arthur's court, and after his time, for a thousand years, kings and knights looked back to him and to his court as to copies of all that was best for themselves to be.

There are many more stories than these that I have told you of King Arthur, of Queen Guinevere, of Sir Lancelot, of Sir Gawain, and of the other knights. There are enough of them to fill many and many books such as this. I should like to think that sometime I might tell you more of them. If the reading of these proves half as pleasant to you as the telling of them has been to me, I trust that I may do so.   Here, for the present, our jour ney and the stories of it must pause.   I have done as well as I hoped to do if you turn away from these stories with as much regret as we felt when we turned away from the land of King Arthur's birth and left behind us the sweet air and the great, glorious rocks, the cries of the sea - birds, the roar and the dash of the water, and all the sights and the sounds of the Cornish shore and the Cornish sea.